Structured Questions for
A Level Physics

TONY YORK
BSc, ARCS
Head of Middle School and former Head of Physics
Alleyn's School, London

Hodder & Stoughton
LONDON SYDNEY AUCKLAND TORONTO

British Library Cataloguing in Publication Data
York, Tony
  Structured questions for A level physics.
  I. Title
  530.076

  ISBN 0–340–51374–8

First published 1991

Typeset by Wearside Tradespools, Fulwell, Sunderland.
Printed in Great Britain for the educational publishing division of Hodder and Stoughton Ltd, Mill Road, Dunton Green, Sevenoaks, Kent by Biddles Ltd, Surrey.

CONTENTS

PREFACE

The first GCSE physics students have taken their A levels, and the National Curriculum is with us. In response to these changes, the more advanced studies in physics have also changed. There are interesting courses available at AS level, and some exciting initiatives under the heading '16–19'. All the present examinations at this level contain some element of comprehension or data analysis, often on unfamiliar subject matter, but with the physics content being within the syllabus. Whatever the changes that continue to take place in physics courses, it seems certain that there will still be an emphasis on applications and relevance. The questions in this book are offered with this in mind. The applications are very wide-ranging, from the everyday, through to the latest technology and even to the forefront of physics research. Where relevant, social and environmental aspects have been included.

Some of the questions, particularly in mechanics, are ones where the basic subject matter is encountered at GCSE, and so these can be tackled at quite an early stage in an advanced course. Others will obviously be more appropriate later on, but a few single page (and slightly easier) questions also appear as starters to some topics. The order of the questions follows a progression of subject matter, but as the situations are real their understanding often depends on a combination of topics, and so the questions cannot and should not fall into water-tight compartments.

In addition to the examination aspect of the questions, I very much hope that the situations presented will act as a stimulus to students and teachers. Physics is a subject of practical importance as well as academic interest, being an important basis for technology and engineering. If these questions enlarge pupils' horizons and enable them to see their surroundings with another dimension I will consider the effort well spent.

I would like to acknowledge my debt to many people, particularly to The Ford Motor Company for information and diagrams on ABS braking, automatic transmission and diesel engines; to my optician Mr Lask and to Pilkington for information on the bifocal contact lens; to Keith Waterhouse for kind permission to reproduce part of his article *Baffled!* which first appeared in *Punch* (copyright Keith Waterhouse Ltd, 1968); and to Eric Goodyer of SIRA, Chislehurst for details of the active car suspension.

Tony York

1 Torque wrench

When tightening nuts and bolts on machinery, it is sometimes necessary to tighten them to a precise measurement. For instance, when a car engine is assembled, if the bolts holding the cylinder head on are too loose, oil and water may leak out, and the engine may be badly damaged. If they are over-tightened however the bolts may snap or the threads may be stripped off. A *torque wrench* is the tool used to tighten the nuts and bolts to the precise amount needed. One pattern is shown below.

As the nut becomes more difficult to turn, the effort used to pull on the handle of the wrench actually bends it slightly, and this moves the pointer over the scale. When the pointer reaches the required setting and the nut has *just* stopped turning, the nut has been tightened by the required amount.

(a) Explain how torque (or *turning moment*) is calculated.   (2)
(b) Why does a torque wrench have a long handle?   (2)
(c) Calculate the torque for the wrench shown if the force applied to the end of the handle is 200 N.   (2)
(d) On a sketch of the bent handle show which part is in tension and which in compression.   (2)
(e) Calculate the distance through which the force applied to the end of the handle is moved for one complete turn. Hence calculate the energy transferred if the force is 200 N.   (4)
(f) By means of the screw thread 30% of the energy transferred is used to stretch the tightened bolt. The pitch of the thread is 1.5 mm, so one complete turn only moves the bolt by that much. Calculate how much force is being used to stretch the bolt.   (6)
(g) What happens to the other 70% of the energy transferred?   (2)

Total 20 marks

1

2 Save our skulls!

Climbing frames, swings and slides make children's playgrounds great fun, but of course the children can damage themselves if they fall off. Broken bones usually mend quickly in young children, but severe knocks on the head can be more dangerous because they can cause permanent brain damage. The severity of the impact between a child's skull and the play surface will depend on many factors: the height fallen (and hence the speed of the skull), the duration of the impact (and hence the deceleration), and the rebound height, which can cause 'whiplash' damage to the top of the spine. These factors have been combined into a 'severity index' for a given surface, and a value of about 1000 or above is likely to cause permanent damage. How the severity index varies with the height of the fall is shown in the graph, figure 1, for both concrete and for a specially designed synthetic play surface called 'Ensorb'. Research into the best properties for the material is carried out using life-size models of children with accelerometers inside the skull. The resilience is measured using the pendulum device shown in figure 2. The pendulum is drawn back to a specific height and released. As it rebounds, it uses a low friction ratchet to carry with it a light pointer which records the height of rebound. Until recently the materials used for play surfaces have had a resilience of 40–50% for an impact energy of 0.4 J, but Ensorb reduces this figure to 30%, that is 30% of the impact energy is retained as kinetic energy by the pendulum.

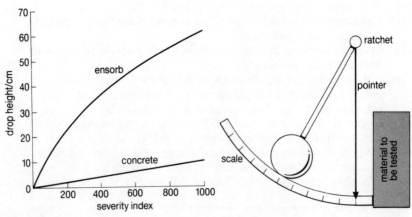

Figure 1   *Figure 2*

(a) On a hard surface a child's skull is brought to a halt in a very short time. Explain why this produces a large force, likely to cause injury. (2)

(b) For a fall from 25 cm, calculate the speed of impact, and if the time for the deceleration is 5 ms, calculate the deceleration of the skull. (The Earth's gravitational field strength is $9.8\,\mathrm{Nkg^{-1}}$.) (4)

(c) Explain in your own words why the resilience of a play surface should be low. (3)

(d) Explain why freshly raked dry sand, as used in long jump pits, is a good surface to reduce the forces involved on impact, and has low resilience. (4)

(e) Ensorb is made by mixing bitumen with synthetic rubber. Bitumen shows a large amount of *plastic* behaviour when stressed. Explain the physical meaning of this term, and why this should make it a suitable material for a play surface. (4)

(f) If the pendulum used in testing has a mass of 0.5 kg, to what height must it be raised to have an 'impact energy' of 0.4 J? To what height will it rebound from Ensorb? What has happened to the 'missing' energy? (6)

(g) In (f) it is necessary to specify the energy because the resilience is not the same (even as a percentage) at different energies. Use your knowledge of elastic and plastic behaviour, and the transition from one to the other to explain whether the resilience of a surface will be more or less at higher energies. (4)

(h) A human skull is obviously different from the spherical steel mass of the pendulum. What differences would change the value obtained for resilience? (3)

Total 30 marks

3 Tyres and ABS braking

Friction between the tyres of a car and the road is needed for traction, braking and steering. The maximum force of friction, F between two surfaces is given by the *normal reaction* multiplied by the *coefficient of friction*, μ. For surfaces which are not sliding over each other, F can take any value from zero up to a maximum (the *limiting* value). If the surfaces do slide over each other, there is still friction, and it is still given by the same relationship, but the value of μ is considerably less than the static value. The forces involved are shown in the simple diagram, figure 1.

To get as much friction as possible, sports cars and racing cars have wide tyres. The side walls of the tyres are very flexible, so that the tread part of the tyre stays as flat as possible in contact with the road. See figure 2. However, this means that the side walls are repeatedly being stretched and relaxed as the car travels along. The stress-strain graph for rubber is shown in figure 3.

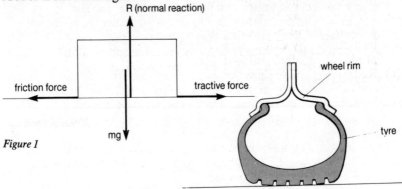

Figure 1

Figure 2

When braking hard, particularly in wet or icy conditions, it is possible for the wheels to lock, i.e. stop turning, which reduces the effectiveness of the braking and also means that steering control is lost. ABS (<u>A</u>nti-lock <u>B</u>raking <u>S</u>ystem) has been developed to overcome this problem. To quote from Ford's literature on the subject:

'This system operates by electromagnetic sensors located at each wheel (figure 4), which monitor road wheel speed. A pulsed signal is sent continuously to two microprocessors at the central control system. When the signal indicates imminent wheel lock, it instantly energises a solenoid that operates a valve, which reduces brake pressure on the affected wheel (or wheels) to avoid lock.

'As the wheel speeds up again, the system recognises this and

4

energises another solenoid/valve assembly which re-applies the brake pressure. This process can happen many times each second.'

The sensor consists of a coil of wire with a small electric current through it, wrapped round a magnetic material. As the toothed wheel, made of iron, passes it, small changes in the current are produced, and these are the 'pulsed signal' referred to above.

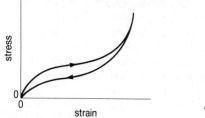

Figure 3

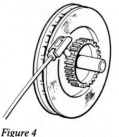

Figure 4

(a) On suitable diagrams, show the direction of the friction force *of the road surface on a tyre* when a car is
   (i) accelerating,
   (ii) braking,
   (iii) cornering at steady speed.
   In each case show also the direction of motion or of turning. *(4)*

(b) For a car of mass 1000 kg, travelling at a speed of 20 m/s^{-1} round a bend of radius 50 m, calculate the total friction force that must be produced by all four tyres. Explain why the force will not be produced equally by all four tyres. *(4)*

(c) Redraw figure 2 to show the shape of the tyre when cornering, and indicate on the diagram in which direction the car is turning. *(3)*

(d) Show that the area under a stress–strain graph corresponds to the energy converted *per unit volume* of the material during the stretching. *(4)*

(e) What is the physical significance of the area enclosed by the stress–strain graph for rubber, and how does this show up in the state of a tyre after a long journey? *(3)*

(f) By considering the relative motion between the road surface and the tyre when the wheels are turning and when they lock, explain why locked wheels mean poor braking and loss of steering control. *(4)*

(g) 'Pumping' the brakes on and off rapidly with the ABS system improves the braking, in spite of the brakes being off for some of the time. Compare the values of μ (static) and μ (dynamic) with the time for which the brakes are on and off. *(4)*

(h) Explain fully, in terms of the flux produced by the current in the coil and any changes in it, why the rotation of the teeth past the sensor produces a 'pulsed signal'. As a tooth approaches the coil, does the current increase or decrease? *(4)*

Total 30 marks

5

4 Sail-boarding or windsurfing

The flow of air round a sail produces the force needed to propel sailing boats and sail-boards (or windsurfers). The variability of the wind, the shape of the sail and the compressibility of air makes sail-boarding very complicated. However, one of the important principles can be understood by considering a much simpler situation. Figure 1 shows an incompressible liquid flowing at a steady rate through a pipe with a narrow section in it.

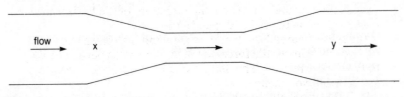

Figure 1

The fluid speeds up to go through the narrow section, and slows down again as the pipe widens. This means that the pressure is *lower* where the fluid is flowing *faster*. This is generally true, even in complicated cases, and is known as the Bernoulli effect.

As well as the force from the wind, a sail-board is acted on by the water. Because it floats so high and is so flat, the water cannot exert much sideways force on the sail-board. Such a sideways force is necessary to make it sail forwards and not drift sideways, so the sail-board has a 'dagger board'. This is a vertical fin which sticks out of the sail-board, down into the water.

The mast is mounted on the sail-board with a 'universal joint' so that it can be tilted in any direction. The diagrams below, figure 2, show the sail-board sailing in the same direction as the wind ('running before the wind'), and sailing at 45° into the wind. It is possible to steer the sail-board by moving the mast and sail backwards or forwards on its universal joint.

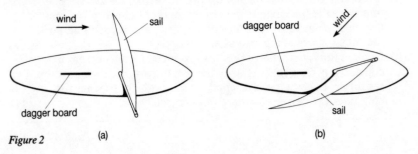

Figure 2

(a) Why, for a steady rate of flow, must the fluid speed up as it goes through the narrow section of the pipe? (2)

(b) What has happened to the kinetic energy of the fluid as it enters the narrow section? (1)

(c) To cause the change in kinetic energy in (b), work must have been done on the fluid; explain how this tells you that there must be a force acting in the direction of flow, and that therefore the pressure is less in the narrow section. (3)

(d) The fluid slows down again as it comes out of the narrow section. Use this fact to explain that the pressure must rise again. (3)

(e) The simple argument developed in questions (a) to (d) might suggest that the pressure is the same at X and Y. Say why, for a real fluid, this cannot be true, even though the speeds are the same. (2)

(f) Copy figure 2a, and on it show the directions of the horizontal forces acting on the sail and sail-board. (2)

(g) If the area of the sail is 1.5 m^2 and the wind is blowing at a speed of 5 ms^{-1}, estimate the force on the sail when it is perpendicular to the wind direction. The density of air is 1.2 kgm^{-3}. State any assumptions you make. (5)

(h) Why is it impossible for a sail-board to sail at the speed of the wind? (2)

(i) When sailing at 45° into the wind, show how the wind flows over the sail. Say where the wind is travelling fastest and slowest with respect to the sail, and hence show any pressure differences across the sail. (4)

(j) On a copy of figure 2b, show the direction of the horizontal forces on the sail and the sail-board from the wind and the water. (2)

(k) When sailing, as in figure 2b, explain carefully what happens to the forces on the sail-board when the mast is tipped (i) forwards and (ii) backwards, and how this leads to the steering of the sail-board. (4)

Total 30 marks

5 Measuring wind speed

An instrument to measure wind speed is called an anemometer. The most common type is shown in figure 1, and consists of three or four small hemi-spherical cups which catch the wind and so turn their support arms around a central spindle. The rotation of the spindle turns a small generator, and the voltage produced is a measure of the wind speed. Of course the cups cannot possibly move at the speed of the wind, because there is some resistance to the rotation. The wind must actually hit the cups to provide the force to overcome the resistance. Nevertheless a voltmeter can be calibrated to show the wind speed directly.

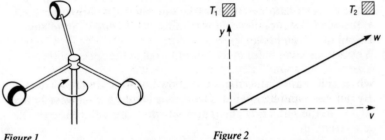

Figure 1

Figure 2

A type of anemometer with no moving parts has been devised using ultrasound. It consists of three arms at right angles to each other, each of which measures the speed of the wind in its own direction, so that the absolute speed and direction can be calculated. One of the arms is shown in figure 2, along with a vector diagram of the wind speed, w, resolved into two components. It has two transducers T_1 and T_2 which alternately give out and receive very short, sharp pulses of sound.

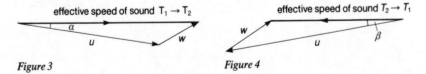

Figure 3

Figure 4

In still air the speed of the sound, u is the same in both directions, but if there is a wind the situation is more complex. The direction of the sound picked up by T_2 from T_1 must obviously be along the direction $T_1 - T_2$, but to achieve this the sound must have started out at an angle α to this and be 'blown back on course'. The speed of sound along $T_1 - T_2$ is the vector sum of u and w, as shown in figure 3. The corresponding vector diagram for a pulse of sound from T_2 to T_1 is shown in figure 4. The times taken for the sound to travel each way are now different and, by measuring them, the component of the wind speed v in direction T_1 to T_2 can be calculated. In practice the calculation is done electronically, and the whole package of ultrasound pulse producer and calculator is miniaturised, robust and maintenance free solid state circuitry. The user simply reads off the wind speed from a digital meter.

(a) Give *three* possible causes of resistance to movement of the first type of anemometer, and say how they can be minimised. (6)

(b) Remembering the anemometer *must* be exposed to the weather, which cause of resistance stated in (a) is likely to change, so altering the calibration? (2)

(c) What is ultrasound, and why is it used in preference to ordinary sound? (2)

(d) Use the vector diagrams to show that the effective speed of sound from T_1 to T_2 is $u \cos \alpha + v$, and that from T_2 to T_1 it is $u \cos \beta - v$. (4)

(e) If the distance between the transducers is d, write down expressions for the times t_1 and t_2 taken for the sound to travel from T_1 to T_2 and from T_2 to T_1 respectively, in terms of u, v, d, α and β. (4)

(f) The speed of sound in air is approximately 320 ms^{-1}. Explain why α and β are very nearly equal for most wind speeds. (4)

(g) By putting α and β equal, and then eliminating $\cos \alpha$, show that

$$v = \frac{d}{2}\left(\frac{1}{t_1} - \frac{1}{t_2}\right)$$

(4)

(h) What advantages does the 'sonic' anemometer have over the traditional type? (4)

Total 30 marks

6 Pumping water for irrigation

The basic design of a 'centrifugal' pump is shown below in figure 1. Water surrounding the impeller is accelerated as the impeller turns, and this water is pumped out through the outlet pipe. Removal of water from the centre of the pump reduces the pressure there, and so more water comes in from the inlet pipe to take its place. The net result is that water has moved from the centre of the pump to the outside, hence the name 'centrifugal'. The vanes of the impeller have to apply force to the water, and are therefore usually reinforced by ribs joining the vanes, as in figure 2. The ribs may even form a complete disc.

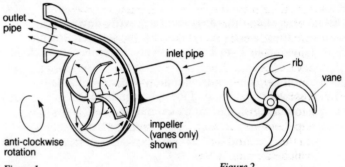

Figure 1

Figure 2

Figure 3 shows two possible types of casing which could be fitted round the impeller. Both have a spiral path, called a 'volute', to take the water away. In both cases, as the water moves around the volute, the pressure is increasing, and this produces an *inward* force on the impeller. The impeller transmits this force to the axle. In the single volute design, the force on the axle is unbalanced, leading to wear of the ball bearings holding the axle. The double volute design gives a balanced force, cutting down on the bearing wear.

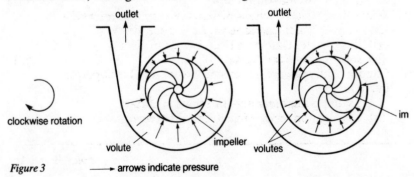

Figure 3   → arrows indicate pressure

A pump used for irrigation may have to lift water from a deep well and pump it into a system of ditches, or it may be used for taking water from a ditch and spraying it directly onto the crops. The pump itself may differ in detailed design, depending on whether it needs to produce high pressure or a large volume flow of water. It could be driven by an electric motor or a gas or diesel engine, depending on where it is to be used.

(a) Describe the magnitude and direction of the force that is needed to make something move in a circle at constant speed. (3)

(b) Consider the part of a vane nearest to the centre. As it turns it pushes on the water in contact with it, so both the vane and the water are moving in similar directions to start with. As they continue to move, the vane travels in a circle, but the water *does not*. Explain why their movements are different in terms of the force you described in (a). (4)

(c) Further out from the centre the vane is still pushing on the water. On a sketch of one vane, show how the vane will bend to provide this force, and hence explain whether the reinforcing ribs are in tension or compression. (4)

(d) How does the water flowing along the volutes (fig. 3) produce an *inward* force on the impeller, and why should this force be as balanced as possible? (4)

(e) As well as the forces mentioned in (a) to (d) above, there is a force on the impeller *along its axis*. By considering the direction of water flow in the inlet and outlet pipes, explain how this force arises and in which direction it acts. (3)

(f) When starting to operate, the pump should be full of water already (i.e. the pump should be *primed*). If the pump is very well made, with very small clearances between the moving parts, it may work without priming, though it will take longer to get started. What is the difference between air and water that explains these observations? (3)

(g) When pumping water from a well the vertical distance from the pump down to the water level cannot be more than about 10 m. Explain what force lifts the water from the well to the pump, and why there is this theoretical limit. (3)

(h) Which of the two variations of design of pump mentioned in the last paragraph of the passage would you use for
    (i) lifting water from a well into irrigation ditches
    (ii) spraying water onto crops? (2)

(i) Choose, with reason(s), a sensible power supply to operate a pump in
    (i) a water pumping station in a town in Britain
    (ii) an irrigation scheme in a third world country. (4)

Total 30 marks

7 Viscosity in the food industry

Some food products, like biscuits, icing and chocolate, are handled in the form of liquids, and then set into solids by baking or cooling. Many food factories are highly automated and so it is important to know the properties of the liquids so that they can be pumped through pipes to where they are wanted. The most important property from this point of view is the *viscosity* of the liquid. Figure 1 shows the flow of liquid through a pipe. The speed of flow is greatest at the middle and slowest at the edges, so there is a *velocity gradient* ($\Delta v/\Delta x$) across the liquid. Figure 2 shows an enlarged three-dimensional section of this flow. 'Layers' of liquid are moving relative to each other and because of friction between them a force F is needed to maintain the flow. A liquid which requires a large force is said to have a high viscosity.

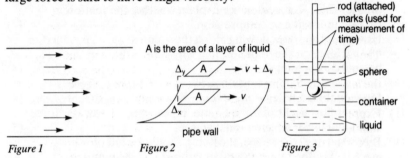

Figure 1 Figure 2 Figure 3

For some simple liquids, $F = \eta A (\Delta v/\Delta x)$ where η is a constant called the viscosity (an equation proposed by Newton)

$$\text{so} \quad \eta = \frac{(F/A)}{(\Delta v/\Delta x)}$$

F/A is the 'shear stress' in the liquid. Since one layer is moving faster than the other, it moves a distance Δy ahead in time Δt, and $\Delta v = \Delta y/\Delta t$. Putting this in the expression for η gives:

$$\eta = \frac{(F/A)}{(\Delta y/\Delta x)/\Delta t}$$

($\Delta y/\Delta x$) is called the 'shear strain', and so ($\Delta y/\Delta x$)/Δt is the rate of shear strain, or just shear rate. For simple liquids the shear rate is therefore proportional to the shear stress. For more complicated liquids, like chocolate, viscosity is defined in the same way, but η is no longer a constant, so a graph of shear stress against shear rate will not be a straight line through the origin. Liquids like this are called 'non-Newtonian'. This means that in any measurement of viscosity, the rate of movement affects the value obtained. A very simple method of measuring viscosity is to time the fall of a sphere through the liquid. The sphere has a rod attached, and the time is taken between two marks on this rod reaching the surface, see figure 3. If the sphere falls slowly enough for the flow round it not to be turbulent, the friction force is $F = 6\pi\eta r v$, where r is the radius of the sphere and v is its velocity of fall. This can result in the sphere falling at a steady velocity, its terminal velocity. As well as the friction force and the weight, there is an upthrust on the sphere from being submerged in the chocolate; this is given by $\frac{4}{3}\pi r^3 \rho_c g$, where ρ_c is the density of the chocolate and g is the Earth's gravitational field strength.

(a) Why does the speed of flow of a liquid vary across the pipe?   (2)
(b) Sketch a graph of shear stress against shear rate for a Newtonian liquid, and one for chocolate, given that a certain minimum stress is needed before chocolate will flow at all.   (3)
(c) A sphere falls from the surface of a viscous liquid. Draw a graph showing the way its speed changes with time as it falls. Explain what forces are acting on it and how they change (if at all).   (3)
(d) Draw a labelled diagram of the forces acting on the sphere when it is falling at terminal velocity.   (3)
(e) The formula given for the friction force surprises most students when they see it for the first time; they expect it to depend on the *area* of the falling sphere, and hence r^2. Show that the formula for the friction force is dimensionally correct.   (3)
(f) Express the weight of the sphere in terms of the density ρ_s of the stainless steel of which it is made, and its radius, r.   (2)
(g) By considering the terminal velocity case, show that the viscosity can be calculated from the other measurements by the relationship:

$$\eta = \frac{2r^2 g (\rho_s - \rho_c)}{9v}$$ (3)

(h) Consider using a sphere of the same stainless steel but twice the radius, in a Newtonian liquid. What happens to the
   (i) weight   (iii) friction force
   (ii) upthrust   (iv) terminal velocity?   (4)
(i) Which answers to (h) would be altered if the liquid was non-Newtonian, and why?   (3)
(j) A more sophisticated measurement of viscosity is sometimes made using a rotating cylinder immersed in the liquid. Draw up a preliminary design for such a viscometer, showing how it can be turned, at varying speeds, and how the force needed to turn it against the resistance of the liquid can be measured.   (4)

Total 30 marks

8   Continuously variable automatic transmission

A petrol engine can only work efficiently over a narrow range of speeds and so cannot drive a car directly, at all the speeds the driver needs. The usual way to overcome the problem is to use a gear box with four or five fixed gear ratios. The driver has to 'change gear' so that the engine can stay within its narrow range. Some cars have 'automatic transmission', where the gears, still with a few fixed ratios, are changed automatically. There have been various 'continuously variable' gearboxes made, one of which is the 'CTX' (Continuously variable TransaXle) from Ford. The engine drives the wheels through a belt which runs round two pulleys which are V shaped in cross-section. The sides of the pulleys can move together, so that the belt effectively has to move round a large diameter pulley, or apart, so that the belt moves round a small diameter pulley. (Since the belt is a fixed length, obviously if one pulley is large the other one must be small.) This is shown in figures 1 and 2, black and white being used to emphasise the pulleys and belt.

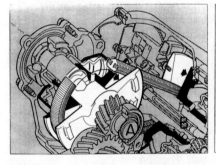

Figure 1   Low gear

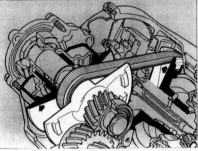

Figure 2   High gear

Belt drives are common in most car engines, e.g. the 'fan belt', and have even been used for automatic transmission before, but they are usually made of some sort of reinforced rubber. Any power they transmit must be with the belt in tension. The belt in the CTX system transmits power in *compression*. The belt consists of 320 shaped steel plates threaded onto two sets of three steel bands, which are each made up of 10 steel loops. In tension, or bending, the plates can separate slightly and the steel bands are flexible, but in compression the plates push flat against each other, making the belt very rigid. This construction is shown as part of figure 1. Driving a car with CTX transmission feels rather different from a fixed ratio gearbox, either manual or automatic, because the engine speed stays almost the same as the car's speed changes. This is shown graphically in figure 3. The lines labelled 1st gear, 2nd gear etc. are for a normal gearbox, for comparison.

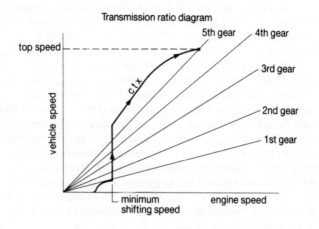

Figure 3

(a) At low speed the engine turns faster than the wheels, and at high speed more slowly. By comparing figures 1 and 2, say which axle, A or B, is connected to the engine. Explain your answer. *(4)*

(b) Explain how the molecular structure of rubber accounts for its low Young's modulus and high flexibility. *(6)*

(c) Why can rubber drive belts only transmit power in *tension*? *(2)*

(d) Why are rubber drive belts reinforced, usually with threads of some sort? *(2)*

(e) The cross-section of the CTX belt is 4 cm², approx., and the Young's modulus for steel is 21×10^{10} Pa and for rubber 0.005×10^{10} Pa, approx. Calculate the percentage stretch for a belt of each material when under a force of 4000 N. *(6)*

(f) Why is the cross-section of the steel bands much smaller than that of the steel plates? *(2)*

(g) Why does having six bands of 10 loops each, like the separate strands in a rope, make the belt more flexible? *(4)*

(h) Draw a graph of car speed against engine speed for a conventional gearbox as the driver goes through each successive gear, up to the same top speed. The 1st to 5th gear lines from figure 3 should be used as a basis. *(4)*

Total 30 marks

15

9 Active car suspension

As a car travels along it is subject to forces from the road surface which change rapidly. Even on a smooth road accelerating, braking and turning lead to different forces at different wheels, and on an uneven surface the forces can be very erratic. A conventional car suspension system uses springs to allow the unevenness to be absorbed without excessive movement of the car body, and the tendency of the system to oscillate is damped down by 'shock absorbers'. Much less movement of the car body, and therefore a smoother ride and better road-holding, are obtained by using 'active' suspension. Sensors on the steering column detect when the car is turning, and sensors on the suspension of each wheel detect whether it is moving towards or away from the car body. Further sensors are connected to the accelerator and the braking system. All this information is fed to a computer which operates hydraulic pumps at each wheel. If a wheel hits a bump in the road the wheel will start to move upwards, towards the body of the car. This movement is detected by the sensor at that wheel, and the hydraulic pump raises the wheel to keep the same force between wheel and body, as in figure 1.

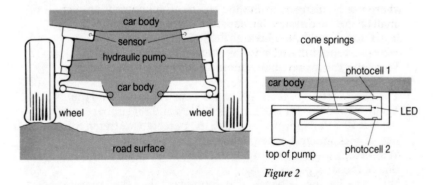

Figure 2

The sensors have been very expensive, but a relatively cheap optical method has now been developed. The principle is shown in cross-section in figure 2. The middle plate moves slightly in response to changes in force from the wheel, and this movement changes the light intensity from the light emitting diode (LED) at the two photocells. The *difference* in voltage from the two photocells is amplified by the differential amplifier shown in figure 3. The cone springs operate in the Hooke's Law region, the difference in light levels is proportional to the movement (for *small* movements) and the voltage output of the photocells is proportional to the light level.

16

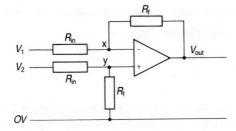

Figure 3

(a) Describe the sequence of events if one wheel of the car falls into a hole in the road (4)

(b) Use the principle of moments to explain why the front of a car dips down if the brakes are applied. How should the hydraulic pumps on the front wheels adjust to compensate for this, so that the car stays level? (6)

(c) What does 'the springs operate in the Hooke's Law region' mean? (2)

(d) A force of 25 kN acting on the pair of cone springs produces a movement of 1 mm. Calculate the movement caused by a force of 10 kN. (2)

(e) Assume that the LED acts like a point source of light, so that the light intensity falling on the photocells,

$$L = \frac{\text{constant}}{r^2}$$

where r is the distance from the LED to each photocell. Let the small change in distance because of a movement of the wheel be δr, so that one photocell becomes distance $r + \delta r$ and the other one $r - \delta r$ from the LED. Write down expressions for the light intensities at the two photocells after the movement, and show that the difference between them is

$$\frac{\text{constant} \times 4\delta r}{r^3}$$

and so is proportional to the movement δr (ignore any terms containing δr^2 as being very small). (6)

(f) State the very good working approximations for the
  (i) current flow into the two inputs of the operational amplifier
  (ii) potential difference between X and Y. (4)

(g) The potential differences across the two photocells are V_1 and V_2 and these are applied across the two inputs of the differential amplifier. Obtain expressions for the potential at Y and the potential at X, and hence show that

$$V_{\text{out}} = -\frac{R_f}{R_{\text{in}}}(V_1 - V_2)$$ (6)

Total 30 marks

10 Diesel versus petrol engines

Diesel engines have been used for a long time in heavy vehicles, like lorries and trains. They were initially unpopular in cars, although cheap to run, because of their unsatisfactory acceleration. This limitation is largely due to the slower running of a diesel engine, which is necessary because of the different method of introducing the fuel.

In a four stroke engine, either diesel or petrol, the piston in its cylinder goes through four complete movements (and so the engine goes through two revolutions) for one operating cycle. As the piston moves down, expanding the gas in the cylinder, the inlet valve opens and a mixture of petrol and air (in the case of a petrol engine) or just air (in the case of a diesel engine) is drawn in. As the piston returns it compresses the gas (with the valves closed). At the end of this compression stroke the fuel burns, and the heat produced expands the gas, which pushes the piston down. The next time the piston moves up the exhaust valve is open and so the burnt fuel is pushed out. The volume change produced in a petrol engine during compression is about 9 : 1, and at the end of this stroke the petrol–air mixture is lit by a spark. The corresponding ratio for a diesel engine is about 20 : 1, but only air is being compressed. The compression produces a high temperature, so that when the fuel is suddenly injected into the cylinder at the end of the compression stroke it spontaneously ignites. In a petrol engine the petrol and air are already thoroughly mixed when the spark ignites the mixture; in a diesel engine when the fuel is injected it has about 6 thousandths of a second to mix with the air and burn.

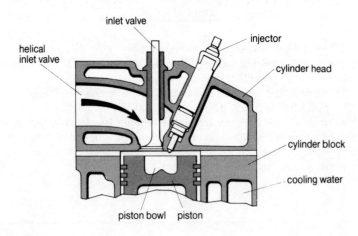

Figure 1

This short time means the fuel has to be injected in the form of very tiny droplets, and there is more air than necessary for the complete burning of the fuel. Therefore a diesel engine is bigger than a petrol engine of the same power. There is also a limit on the speed of the engine, since a faster running engine would give even less time for the mixing of the fuel with the air. To help with the mixing the air is swirled around by the specially shaped air inlet port as it is drawn into the cylinder, and is further swirled as it is compressed by the shaped piston bowl, shown in the diagram.

(a) Show that the mechanical power transferred by a force is equal to force × speed. (2)

(b) Explain in molecular terms why the temperature of a gas increases as it is compressed. (2)

(c) What assumptions about the molecules of a gas are made in deriving the ideal gas equation, $pV = \frac{1}{3}nmc^2$ (4)

(d) Use the ideal gas equation to calculate the pressure in a cylinder of a diesel engine at the end of a compression stroke. Assume that the air is taken in at atmospheric pressure (10^5 Pa), at a temperature of 27 °C, and is heated by the compression to 477 °C. (4)

(e) Explain why it would be totally inappropriate to apply the ideal gas equation to the compression stroke of a petrol engine. (3)

(f) The 'compression ratio' for a petrol engine is much lower than for a diesel engine and so there is less heating on compression. What might happen to the petrol–air mixture if there was too much compression? (2)

(g) Lead is used in some petrol to prevent premature ignition of the mixture. Give *two* reasons why unleaded petrol is becoming more popular. (3)

(h) If improvements in the design of fuel injectors for diesel engines mean that the droplets can have half their previous diameter, how many times more droplets will there be for a given volume of fuel? (4)

(i) By what factor has the total surface area of the fuel droplets increased as a result of the change in (h), and why does this lead to more efficient burning? (4)

(j) Diesel engines are more efficient than petrol engines, but even so are less than 30% efficient overall. By considering the diagram, suggest where a lot of the wasted internal energy of the hot gas might go. (2)

Total 30 marks

11   Air gun

The basic principle of an air gun is shown in the diagram. The spring is
compressed by a lever (not shown) and held in place by the trigger
mechanism (also not shown). When the trigger is pulled the spring is
released, and pushes the piston along the cylinder which compresses the
air; the compressed air in turn pushes the pellet out of the barrel.

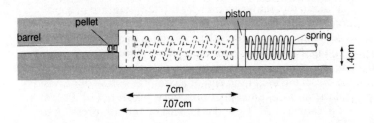

> Data: Some typical figures for an air gun (0.177 calibre) are given
> below:
> mass of pellet = 5×10^{-4} kg
> muzzle velocity = 200 ms^{-1}
> radius of cylinder = 1.4 cm
> length of cylinder = 7.07 cm
> travel of piston = 7.00 cm

(a) Show that the kinetic energy of a pellet fired from the gun is less
    than the legal maximum of 13 J.   (2)
(b) Calculate the volume of the air in the cylinder before and after
    the trigger is pulled. (Assume that the pellet does not start to
    move until the air is fully compressed.)   (4)
(c) Taking atmospheric pressure as 10^5 Pa, calculate the pressure of
    the air when it is compressed. (Assume that there is no
    temperature change.)   (3)
(d) Explain why the temperature of the air in fact rises as it is
    compressed.   (3)
(e) Very approximately, the energy transferred in compressing the
    air is given by: ½ × pressure change × volume change. Show that
    this has the correct units (J) and work out its value.   (4)
(f) Estimate the overall efficiency of the air gun and explain why it
    is so low.   (4)

Total 20 marks

12   Gas cylinders

Cylinders that contain gas, or, when newly filled, a mixture of gas and liquid, are very common portable energy stores. They are used in camping stoves, for blow lamps, for caravans, heating tar for roads, etc. Propane, C_3H_8, is one of the gases used, and has a relative molecular mass of 44. At 'normal' temperature and pressure 44 g of propane would occupy about 24 litres. During use the pressure of gas delivered from a cylinder is remarkably constant because as more gas is used more liquid evaporates to take its place.

A gas cylinder used in roadworks contained 47 kg of gas when newly filled, and had a diameter of 0.4 m and a height of 1.5 m. It was noticed that while being used to operate a burner the cylinder itself became very cold, to the extent that frost (tiny ice crystals) appeared on the outside of the cylinder, but only on the *bottom* part of the cylinder.

(a) Calculate the volume of 47 kg of propane at 'normal' temperature and pressure. (2)

(b) Calculate the volume of the cylinder. (volume $V = \pi r^2 h$, where r is radius and h is height of cylinder.) (2)

(c) If the 47 kg of gas was compressed into the cylinder with no temperature change, and *without changing into a liquid*, calculate the final pressure inside the cylinder. (2)

(d) In fact the gas *does* partially liquify (you can hear the liquid if you shake a new cylinder). Use your knowledge of the molecular state of liquids and gases to explain why this leads to a much smaller pressure than that calculated in (c). (3)

(e) Explain why it takes longer than normal for a camping gas stove to heat water on a very cold morning. (3)

(e) As gas is used from the cylinder some of the liquid evaporates. Explain in molecular terms why this cools the liquid surface. (3)

(f) Why does the cooling at the liquid surface quickly cool all the rest of the liquid? (2)

(g) Explain the frosting of the cylinder described in the passage. (3)

Total 20 marks

13 The toughness of biological materials

In man-made engineering structures cracks are a common cause of failure. If a material is under tension the crack may spread; whether it does or not depends on several factors such as the tensile stress in the material, the depth and tip radius of the crack, and whether the material has any mechanism for relieving the stress concentration at the tip of the crack. For a crack to spread, new surfaces are being produced in the material, and this needs energy; the energy is transferred from the strain energy stored in the material. In some cases this transfer of energy can be almost explosive, as in a shattering car windscreen, a bursting balloon, or a towing cable snapping.

Biological materials under stress have various ways of preventing the spread of cracks. Hard materials like bone and shell are natural composites. They are reinforced with fibres which are themselves strong but relatively brittle, and are weakly bonded into a softer matrix. A crack spreading through the material is deflected at the interface between the matrix and the fibre, and so the tip radius increases enormously as in figure 1. As this new crack is along the direction of tensile stress it does not have the same tendency to spread. (Many people will not feed chicken bones to their dogs because of their tendency to splinter in this way.)

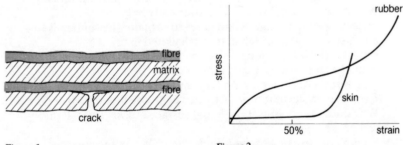

Figure 1

Figure 2

Soft biological materials, like skin, manage to be tough in a different way. The graphs show the stress/strain curves for rubber and skin. They both have long chain molecules which are normally kinked or coiled, and these are relatively easy to uncoil but much more difficult to stretch once they are in this state. However, in the case of skin, these molecules, which are of collagen are embedded in a matrix of elastin, which is very flexible, and so their strength does not come into play until there is considerable strain.

The energy stored in the skin of a bat's wing, stretched between the 'fingers' is low, so the skin does not tear easily even if punctured; in fact the bat can go on flying and the puncture will still heal if it is small. Contrast this with a pin prick in the stretched rubber of an inflated balloon!

(a) Explain the scientific meaning of *tough*, *brittle*, *plastic* and *elastic*. (6)

(b) Sketch the shape of a stress/strain graph for a ductile metal like copper or mild steel. (4)

(c) Explain in molecular terms the difference between the elastic and plastic behaviour in the graph you sketched for (b). (4)

(d) In metals, what is the 'mechanism for relieving the stress concentration at the tip of the crack'? (2)

(e) Show that the area under a stress/strain graph gives the energy per unit volume transferred in stretching a material. (2)

(f) Compare the energy stored in stretched skin and in stretched rubber, both up to 50% strain, and use this comparison, and the information in the passage, to explain why skin is much less susceptible to cracks spreading. (6)

(g) In fact all the energy transferred in stretching a material may *not* be available when it is relaxed or it breaks. To your sketch graph for a ductile metal add a line showing the behaviour as the stress is removed, after the elastic limit has been passed, and shade in the area representing the energy per unit volume which cannot be recovered. What has happened to this energy? (6)

Total 30 marks

14 Domestic and commercial cookers

There are many types of cooker available, though the most common can be classified as either gas or electric, with several alternative electric types. As the different types are often in competition, there are conflicting advertising claims made about them: gas cookers are generally claimed to be faster and more controllable, but recent developments in electric cookers have enabled them to rival this claim. Electric cookers are often said to be 'cleaner'.

Four methods of heating a pan are shown in figures 1 to 4.

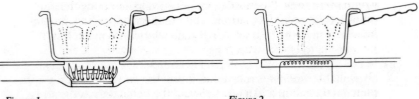

Figure 1   Figure 2

The first is a conventional gas cooker, where the burning gas heats the base of the pan directly. However, all is not as simple as it may seem. When boiling water, the base of the pan in contact with the flame cannot be much above 100 °C, but the hottest part of the flame may be at several hundred degrees. There is therefore a temperature gradient across the gas next to the pan, and the energy from the flame has to pass through this 'boundary layer'.

Figure 2 shows a solid-plate type of electric heater. The heating element is a helix of nichrome wire embedded in a steel plate. The energy from the element has to pass through the plate and then through the pan to reach the water, and ideally the pan should have a base which is machined very flat. This type of cooker has the slowest response, but may be very good for simmering and 'slow cookers'.

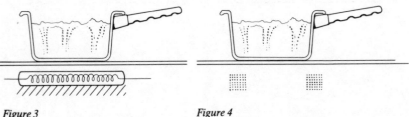

Figure 3   Figure 4

The next diagram, figure 3, shows a much faster electric cooker. The basis of the heating is a medium wave quartz tube. The heating element itself gets very hot (950 °C) and gives out infra-red radiation with a wavelength of about 2.6 μm. This radiation passes through the quartz tube and the ceramic hob and strikes the base of the pan. The heating and cooling time for the tube is only 30 s.

Finally, figure 4 shows a type of cooker where the only things to be heated are the pan and its contents! A coil beneath the cooker surface is supplied with a high frequency alternating current which produces a rapidly alternating magnetic field. This field generates currents in the material of the pan itself, so the pan is heated directly.

(a) Explain why the temperature of the outside of a metal pan containing boiling water cannot be much above 100 °C, whatever form of heating is used. (2)

(b) Turning up the gas flame so that it just covers the base of the pan would seem to be the most economical way of heating the pan quickly. Use the information in the passage to explain why the heating is quicker if an even higher flame is used, even though it might seem that the extra energy escapes uselessly round the sides. (3)

(c) By what method does the energy reach the pan for the solid-plate type of cooker, and why should the pan have a flat base? (3)

(d) Why must the heating element in a solid-plate cooker *not* touch the steel of the plate? What electrical and thermal properties should the material that separates them have? (4)

(e) Why is the solid-plate cooker the slowest to respond to changes? (2)

(f) In the infra-red cooker, why must the tube and the cooker top be made of quartz, and why is the underside of the quartz tube silvered, as shown in figure 3? (4)

(g) For the type of cooker shown in figure 4, sketch the shape of the magnetic field produced by the coil
    (i) without a pan on the cooker
    (ii) with an iron pan on the cooker. (4)

(h) Pans are made from iron, stainless steel, aluminium alloy, copper and glass. Choose the best pan material for each cooker, explaining your choice. If there is no preference for a particular cooker explain why, and if a material is totally unsuitable also explain why. (8)

Total 30 marks

15 Acoustic strain gauge

Measuring *strain* is important for a whole range of different engineering applications. The most usual method is to measure the change in resistance of a metal as it is stretched, as described in detail in the 'Strain gauge' question, number 27. Difficulties arise in some situations where the strain in a rapidly moving object is needed, such as the propeller shaft of a large ship. Such a shaft has to transmit large turning forces from the engine to the propeller, but also is subject to large compression forces. The behaviour of the metal of the shaft in these conditions is monitored using acoustic strain gauges, the principle of which is shown in figure 1.

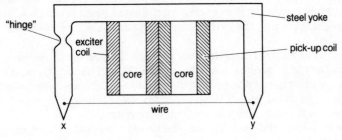

Figure 1

The steel yoke is tightly clamped to the shaft so that the hardened steel points X and Y dig into it. As the metal of the shaft compresses or twists the points X and Y move closer or further apart, and so alter the natural frequency of oscillation of the wire. The wire is made to oscillate by the magnetic field from the exciter coil, and its oscillation is detected by the pick-up coil. The current in the pick-up coil is used to control the frequency of the amplifier which operates the exciter coil, and so the oscillations become tuned to the natural frequency of the wire.

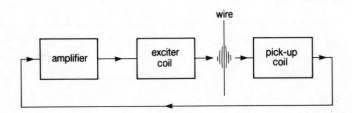

Figure 2

Figure 2 shows a block diagram of the process. The advantage of this system over a conventional strain gauge is that the oscillation frequency can be used to modulate the amplitude of the radio waves from a small radio transmitter, also mounted on the rotating shaft, and the signals can be picked up and analysed *with no direct contact with the rapidly turning shaft*.

Data: density of steel $= 8 \times 10^3 \, \mathrm{kg m^{-3}}$
Young's modulus of steel $= 2 \times 10^{11} \, \mathrm{Nm^{-2}}$
frequency of fundamental transverse oscillation of a
stretched wire $= \dfrac{1}{2l} \sqrt{\dfrac{T}{m}}$
where l = length of wire, T = tension in wire and m = mass per unit length of wire

---

(a) Give the scientific definition of the term *strain*. (1)
(b) By considering the forces produced by a propeller on the water, and hence how the ship is propelled, explain why a propeller shaft is in a state of compression along its length. (4)
(c) The hardened points of the strain gauge make small holes in the shaft. Explain why this does not affect the strength of a metal shaft significantly, but would have disastrous consequences in some materials, such as glass or ceramics. (4)
(d) A steel wire of length 5 cm and radius 0.2 mm is stretched by 5×10^{-3} cm to mount it in the strain gauge. Calculate
  (i) the strain in the wire
  (ii) the stress in the wire
  (iii) the tension in the wire
  (iv) the mass per unit length of the wire
  (v) the fundamental frequency of oscillation of the wire. (8)
(e) The points X and Y subsequently move closer by 2.5×10^{-3} cm because of the compressing of the shaft. Calculate the new tension, and show that the percentage changes in l and m are insignificant by comparison with the percentage change in T. (4)
(f) Calculate the new frequency after the movement in (e). (2)
(g) Why are the exciter coil and the pick-up coil mounted side by side on separate cores, and not concentrically on the same core? (2)
(h) Use a simple sketch to show what is meant by 'the oscillation frequency can be used to modulate the amplitude of the radio waves from a small radio transmitter'. (2)
(i) Suggest a simple way in which a *resistance* strain gauge on a rotating shaft could be connected to its measuring equipment, and say why you think this is unlikely to be satisfactory. (3)

Total 30 marks

16   Colours in nature

Nature produces many colours in plants and animals, some rather drab for camouflage, and some very bright for mating displays. There are two quite different ways in which the colours may be achieved; one uses pigments which absorb light selectively and only reflect the colour seen; the other uses a thin layer of transparent material which gives the colour by interference.

The way a pigment works can be understood by considering figure 1, which represents a molecule of hydrogen chloride (HCl). Its behaviour is like that of two masses joined by a spring. The charges can be excited into oscillation by an electric field which oscillates at the right frequency, and this field can be provided by electromagnetic radiation. It therefore follows that hydrogen chloride will strongly absorb radiation of a particular wavelength, which happens to be in the infra-red part of the spectrum at 3.3×10^{-6} m. The biological molecules in natural pigments are much more complex, but the absorption of particular colours is still done by charges within the molecule, though sometimes these charges are electrons. In some cases electrons are freed from particular molecules so that light can cause chemical reactions, as in photosynthesis in the pigment chlorophyll, whose absorption spectrum is shown in figure 2.

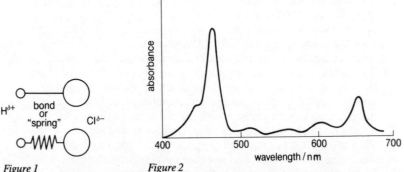

Figure 1   *Figure 2*

The very bright, irridescent colours of some insects' wings are not caused by pigmentation, but by interference. The surface of the wing is covered in a thin transparent layer. Light reflects off the top and the bottom of this layer, as shown in figure 3, and so the light entering the viewers' eyes will have travelled along various different paths. Some wavelengths of light will be in phase, and some will be out of phase and so will cancel. What is seen is the spectrum of white light minus the colours that have interfered destructively, so the colours are always mixtures and not pure spectrum colours.

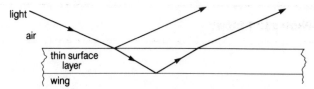

light

air

thin surface
layer

Figure 3 wing

You will almost certainly have seen the same colours in soap bubbles when washing anything and in oily patches spilled on a road when it rains. Both are caused by thin films: a soap bubble is a thin layer of transparent liquid, and a thin layer of oil from the spill floats on the water surface.

(a) Calculate the frequency of electromagnetic radiation which is absorbed by hydrogen chloride. The speed of electromagnetic radiation is $3 \times 10^8 \text{ ms}^{-1}$. *(2)*

(b) The relative atomic mass of hydrogen is 1 and that of chlorine is 35.5. Explain why it is a satisfactory approximation to treat the oscillation of the HCl molecule as if just the hydrogen atom moves. *(3)*

(c) If the mass of a hydrogen atom is 1.7×10^{-27} kg, calculate the stiffness constant of the H—Cl bond. The frequency of oscillation of a mass-spring system is given by

$$f = \frac{1}{2\pi} \sqrt{\frac{k}{m}} \ ,$$

where k is stiffness constant and m is mass. *(4)*

(d) Hydrogen fluoride is similar to hydrogen chloride, except that fluorine has a relative atomic mass of 19 and the H—F bond is approximately twice as stiff as the H—Cl bond. Calculate the wavelength at which HF absorbs radiation. *(3)*

(e) For a pigment to give colours in the visible spectrum, should the frequency be greater or less than that for HCl? *(2)*

(f) If the forces on the particles are similar, why is the movement of electrons rather than ions in a molecule likely to give absorption in the visible part of the spectrum? *(2)*

(g) You probably already know that chlorophyll is green. Use its absorption spectrum to explain why it is green. *(3)*

(h) Use sketches to show waves that are 'in phase' and 'out of phase'. If your sketches represent light waves, how much light is detected in each case? *(4)*

(i) In figure 3 why does the light bend as it enters the transparent layer? *(2)*

(j) Use carefully drawn diagrams like figure 3 to explain why the colour of an insect's wing changes slightly when looked at from different angles. *(5)*

Total 30 marks

17   Radar speed trap

The police use radar to measure the speed of vehicles, and so see if they are obeying the speed restrictions which may be in force. The apparatus consists of a radar source (i.e. a source of electromagnetic radiation with a wavelength of a few centimetres) and a receiver. These two parts are usually built into the same device. The radar waves travel out to a car, and some of them are reflected back into the receiver. However, because the car is moving, the reflected waves do not have the same *frequency* as the waves which were emitted, and the difference is a function of the speed of the car. A comparison of the original frequency and the frequency of the waves that return is made by simply combining them (in suitable proportions). This produces a beat frequency, which is converted electronically into a meter reading, calibrated directly to give the speed of the car.

To understand the relationship between speed and change in frequency, consider the situation from the point of view of the car. A wave crest from the transmitter arrives at a time t'_1, and the next crest arrives at time t'_2. From this point of view the time interval between one crest and the next, i.e. the period of the waves, is

$$T' = t'_2 - t'_1 \tag{1}$$

However, during this time interval, the car has been moving towards the source of waves, at a speed v, and has therefore covered a distance s. The electromagnetic radiation travels at a speed c, and so would take a time t to cover this distance. The car driver would therefore calculate that if he had been stationary the second wave crest would have taken longer to reach him, by this amount, and so the period of waves being emitted, T, is longer than T';

$$T = T' + t \tag{2}$$

which leads to

$$T = T'(1 + v/c) \tag{3}$$

Since the frequency of the waves is $1/T$, it follows that the frequency relationship is

$$f' = f(1 + v/c) \tag{4}$$

where f is the frequency of the waves being emitted, and f' is the frequency of the waves as received by the moving car. This is known as the Doppler shift. The waves reflected from the car are of this same increased frequency, and the difference in frequency, giving rise to the beat frequency and the final meter reading, is in direct proportion to the speed of the car;

$$f' - f = fv/c \tag{5}$$

Data: 1 mile = 1610 m approx.
speed of light $c = 3 \times 10^8$ ms^{-1}
wavelength of radar waves used = 3 cm

(a) Express the distance s in terms of v and T'. (Line 23) (2)
(b) Express the time t in terms of v, c and T'. (2)
(c) Hence show that equation (3) is correct. (2)
(d) From equation (3), show that (4) and (5) follow. (4)
(e) Show that a speed limit of 40 mph is approximately 18 ms^{-1}. (2)
(f) Calculate the frequency of the radar waves. (2)
(g) For a speed limit of 40 mph, calculate the change in frequency of the radar waves. (2)
(h) If the frequency difference rises to 750 Hz, by how much is the car breaking the speed limit? (2)
(i) Why would it be difficult for the police to use the radar speed trap effectively on a winding road, or if there was a lot of traffic? (4)
(j) Explain how two waves of roughly the same amplitude, but slightly different frequencies, lead to 'beats' when combined. (3)
(k) Why is only a tiny proportion of the emitted wave combined with the reflected wave to give the beat frequency? (2)
(l) Sound waves are also subject to the Doppler effect. Describe qualitatively how the note from a racing car engine changes pitch as it approaches, passes and goes away from an observer standing on the racetrack side. (3)

Total 30 marks

18   Microwave satellite communication

The use of satellites for communication using microwaves is relatively commonplace, for example in telephone links. The most useful sort of satellite orbit is a *geostationary* or *geosynchronous* one, because the microwave transmitting and receiving dishes do not have to track, but can constantly point in the same direction.

Communication to and from moving ships and aircraft over long distances is obviously more difficult, even with geostationary satellites. Large ships move relatively slowly, and can carry a transmitting dish and the tracking equipment to keep it pointing in the right direction (assuming they know where they are on the Earth's surface accurately enough!). But small boats and aircraft have a weight and size problem; aircraft have the added complication of high speeds.

A new sort of microwave transmitter (and receiver) has been developed which can transmit in almost any carefully controlled direction without any moving parts, making it lighter and less vulnerable to mechanical damage than a conventional dish. The principle is shown in the diagram.

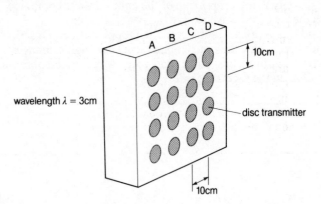

Figure 1

Each disc is a microwave transmitter, but each one can have a different *phase difference* introduced into the signal before it is transmitted. For instance, if all the signals are in phase, there will be a strong signal sent directly in front of the array, but if the top row is 3 cycles, the next row down 2 cycles and the next row 1 cycle behind the bottom row, a strong signal is sent upwards at an angle of about 17°. (This is very similar to the way in which a diffraction grating works for light.) Care has to be taken in choosing the diameter of the discs, and their spacing in the array, otherwise there could be very little signal in some directions.

Data: radius of Earth = 6400 km (approx.)
gravitational field strength at surface of Earth = 10 N kg^{-1}

(a) What time must a geosynchronous satellite take to orbit the Earth once? (2)

(b) Explain why a geosynchronous orbit must be above the equator. (3)

(c) Your answer to (a) enables you to express the speed of the satellite in terms of the radius of its orbit. The data given above enables you to calculate 'GM' for the Earth (universal gravitational constant × mass of Earth). By equating the gravitational force on the satellite to the centripetal force needed to keep it in orbit, show that the radius of a geosynchronous orbit is approximately 42 600 km. (5)

(d) Estimate (possibly by scale drawing) how many degrees north from the equator a receiving dish can be and still 'see' the satellite. (3)

(e) Suggest very briefly, in principle, and without technical details, how a ship's communication with satellites could be used as a navigation aid (so that they *would* know accurately enough where they were!). (3)

(f) Show that the angle of 17° given in the passage is correct. (2)

(g) At what angle, and in what direction, would there be a strong beam if the phase relationships were as follows; vertical column A all in phase, Column B all ⅓ of a cycle later, column C all ⅔ of a cycle later, column D all 1 cycle later? (4)

(h) A single microwave dish has to be many wavelengths in diameter to send a narrow beam in a precise direction. In the 'phased array' set up, it is essential that each disc is only a few wavelengths across. Explain why there is this difference. (4)

(i) Explain how the directional variation of the emission of microwaves from a single disc could lead to the problem mentioned in the last sentence of the passage. (4)

Total 30 marks

19   Locating cable faults

In any long length of electrical cable, as in telephone wires or power cables, faults may develop. The fault has to be located so that the digging needed to repair an underground cable can be done in the right place. One method of finding the fault uses a high frequency voltage pulse producer. The output of the pulse producer as seen on a cathode ray oscilloscope (CRO) screen is shown in figure 1. When this voltage output is applied to the end of the cable, it is modified in several ways. The pulse travels down the cable at high speed and is partially reflected from any fault, or completely reflected if the conductor is broken. The simulated CRO trace in figure 2 shows the rather extreme case of a crack in the conductor, a fault where the insulation round the cable has been damaged, and a total break in the conductor, in that order, and all in the same cable!

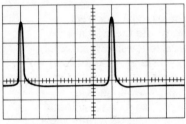

Figure 1   Slower time base

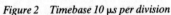

Figure 2   Timebase 10 μs per division

(a) The time-base in figure 2 is set at 10 μs per division. Estimate the time intervals between the original pulse and each of the reflections. Say which part of the pulses you used and why, and give a sensible uncertainty in the results. (8)

(b) If the speed of the pulse was 2×10^8 ms^{-1} calculate how far away each of the faults is, and say how accurately this distance was known. (4)

(c) A fault is located, but when a repair team dig down to the cable they do *not* find the fault (not too surprising in view of your answer to (b)). Briefly outline any method they could now use to locate the fault more accurately. (4)

(d) Explain the difference in height between the original pulse and the pulse when applied to the end of the cable. (2)

(e) Why is there a limit to the length of cable in which faults can be detected by this method? (2)

Total 20 marks

20 Sugar concentration

Workers in the sugar industry routinely measure the concentration of sugar solutions by putting a sample in a *polarimeter*. This consists of a tube with transparent end windows, through which a beam of light is shone. The first window is a polariser, that is it only lets through light with its electric field oscillation in one direction. The sugar solution then rotates this plane of polarisation by an angle depending on the concentration of the solution, and on the wavelength of the light. The other end window through which the light is viewed is also a piece of polaroid, called the detector, which can be rotated on an accurately marked scale. With no sugar solution in the tube the two polaroids should be parallel to let maximum light through, or aligned at 90° to let no light through. With sugar solution present the same thing happens, but at a different angle. The variation of brightness of the light with angle is shown in figure 1.

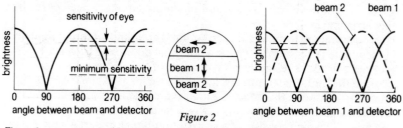

Figure 1   *(Arrows show direction of electric field)*   *Figure 2*   *Figure 3*

It is not easy in practice to judge accurately when the light is at its brightest, or when it is at its darkest, so a more complicated polariser can be used, shown in figure 2. The light now consists of two beams polarised at 90° to each other. It is possible to judge much more accurately when the two parts of the beam are the *same* brightness as each other, as shown in figure 3.

(a) Why is light of a single wavelength used with a polarimeter? (2)
(b) Explain why it is difficult to be sure of the exact position of the
    (i) brightest and (ii) least light. (4)
(c) Sketch what the two beams will look like at the angles of (i) 0°
    and (ii) 90° on figure 3. (3)
(d) Estimate the uncertainty in measuring the angle for the (i)
    darkest, (ii) brightest and (iii) same light intensity. (6)

Total 15 marks

21 Optoelectronics

When light passes through a transparent material its speed changes. This is an extremely well known effect which leads to the light possibly changing direction, or being refracted, as in lenses and prisms. However, there are some interesting materials where other effects take place; in some, called non-linear materials, the speed of the light depends on an electric field which can be applied to the material, either externally or from the electric field of the light itself.

A light wave can be visualised as a travelling, oscillating combination of electric and magnetic fields. As this passes through a material, charges (mainly the electrons) in the molecules respond to the oscillating electric field by oscillating themselves. Some molecules contain electrons which can move along practically the whole length of the molecule. The oscillating electrons then re-radiate the light, and so it is passed through the material. If the molecules in which the electrons oscillate have uneven distribution of charge along their length, the oscillations of the electrons may not be simple, and the speed of the light may be changed.

If the asymmetric molecules can be lined up in the material, applying an electric field by simply placing a potential difference across the material will shift the equilibrium position of the electrons, and so increase the 'non-linear' effects, including a change in the speed of the light. This is used in the 'Mach-Zender interferometer', a device for switching light on and off very quickly. The device uses a waveguide (see figure 1) which consists of a strip of non-linear material with a high refractive index, surrounded by materials with a low refractive index, for instance air and the substrate. The waveguide divides and one arm passes between electrodes so that an electric field can be applied. This alters the speed of the light beam in one branch and if the change in speed is correct, when the beams recombine they interfere destructively so that no light emerges. See figure 2.

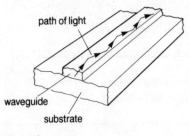

path of light

waveguide

substrate

Figure 1

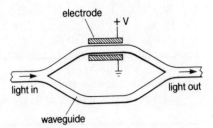

electrode   + V

light in   light out

waveguide

Figure 2

Applying pulses of the correct voltage to the electrodes will produce pulses of light, and this is just what is needed to send coded information along optical fibres, as in modern telephone lines. Another possible future use of optoelectronics is in making 'light computers'. The presence of light could represent logic state 1, and the absence of light logic state 0. The attraction is that the waveguides and 'switches' could be miniaturised much more than the present 'chips' used in computers; since light in one tiny wave guide would not affect light in neighbouring waveguides, whereas electrons flowing in tiny conducting paths within a chip do affect electrons in neighbouring conducting paths.

(a) The passage says that light *may possibly* change direction as a result of a change in speed. In what circumstance does it *not* change direction? (2)
(b) For a monochromatic (single wavelength), plane polarised beam of light, sketch a graph showing the variation of electric field strength with time. (3)
(c) In which direction, relative to your sketch graph for (b), will electrons in the molecules try to move? (2)
(d) Non-linear, or polar, molecules can be thought of as molecules with a positive charge at one end and a negative charge at the other. Why would such molecules be difficult to line up in the same direction, for instance as they crystallised from liquid to solid? How would letting them solidify in a strong electric field help? (4)
(e) Explain how the light stays in a wave guide (figure 1), and how the light can bend round corners in the wave guide. (4)
(f) What phase difference between the beams of light in the Mach-Zender interferometer will produce no light output? What must be happening to the energy of the incoming light? (4)
(g) Light with a wavelength of 600 nm and speed $2 \times 10^8 \ \mathrm{ms^{-1}}$ in the material of the wave guide is used, and the path between the electrodes is 1.2 mm long. Calculate
   (i) how many waves there are between the electrodes with no electric field
   (ii) how many waves there are between the electrodes when the speed is reduced to give no output (as in question (f))
   (iii) the new, reduced speed of the light between the electrodes. (6)
(h) In what *two* ways could electrons flowing in conducting paths influence electrons in other paths in a chip. Why would light in an optical computer not have these disadvantages? (5)

Total 30 marks

22   Lasers

LASER stands for Light Amplification by the Stimulated Emission of Radiation, which is slightly misleading since a laser is a light generator rather than an amplifier. An ordinary light bulb has a heated filament in which each atom gives out its own light, so the total beam of light is extremely chaotic, or *incoherent*. In a laser the atoms are given energy, raising electrons to higher energy levels. Some of these levels are *metastable*, that is the electrons stay in their excited state for a short time. When one does drop back to its lowest level a photon is emitted. Spontaneously emitted photons are reflected along the laser material and back by mirrors at the ends, and these photons trigger, or stimulate, the drop in energy level of other electrons still in the metastable state. The beam now travelling along the axis of the laser has all the waves in step, i.e. it is *coherent*. These differences are illustrated in figures 1 and 2.

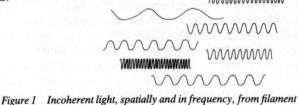

Figure 1   Incoherent light, spatially and in frequency, from filament

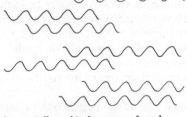

Figure 2   Coherent light, spatially and in frequency, from laser

The energy to raise the electrons to their metastable energy levels can be provided in various ways. The simplest is in the laser diode, where a direct current through the diode provides the energy. A laser diode may be made of gallium arsenide doped with aluminium (AlGaAs) which gives light of 807 nm wavelength, but this light is not very bright or very coherent. However the light can be used to transfer energy to, or 'pump', a laser made of a crystal of neodymium-doped yttrium aluminium garnet (Nd:YAG) a few millimetres long, which can emit light at wavelengths of 1320 nm, 1064 nm and 947 nm. (All wavelengths quoted are in air.) This produces much more coherence, to the extent that several laser diodes, which are not coherent with each other, can

pump the same Nd:YAG laser, so giving a much bigger power output.
The principle is shown in figure 3.

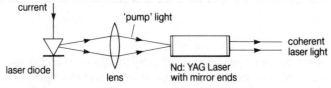

Figure 3

The system described above is quite efficient, the laser diode being
about 25% efficient at transferring electrical energy to light, and the
Nd:YAG laser transferring about 40% of this light into the more
coherent output. It is very reliable because it is all solid-state and has no
moving parts, and is quite compact. However, it cannot be miniaturised
indefinitely, since the beam must be parallel inside the laser, and a very
narrow beam spreads through diffraction. This drawback can be
overcome by making the laser material into the core of an optical fibre,
so that the beam is confined by total internal reflections in spite of the
diffraction spreading.

(a) Why must the laser diode emit light of a *shorter* wavelength than
   any of the emissions from the Nd:YAG laser? *(2)*
(b) Calculate the energy of a photon of light from the laser diode.
   Take Planck's constant as 6.6×10^{-34} Js and the speed of light as
   3×10^8 ms^{-1}. *(2)*
(c) Calculate the frequencies of the three wavelengths emitted by
   the Nd:TAG laser. *(6)*
(d) Say how the wavelengths will be different from the values
   quoted in the passage, when they are inside the material of the
   laser. Will the frequencies be different? *(4)*
(e) Calculate the three electron energy level transitions which give
   rise to the three possible emissions. *(6)*
(f) Show that the overall efficiency of the solid state laser system in
   transferring electrical energy to light is about 10%. *(2)*
(g) The angle θ of the first minimum in the diffraction pattern
   caused by a circular aperture, diameter b, is given by
   $\sin \theta = 1.2\lambda/b$. If the laser has a diameter of 4×10^{-6} m,
   calculate this angle for the shortest wavelength from the
   Nd:YAG laser, and show that it causes a spreading of about
   1.8 mm in a laser only 3 mm long. *(4)*
(h) Will the other wavelengths spread more or less than the one in
   question (g)? *(2)*
(i) Show on a diagram how total internal reflection keeps the beam
   within the laser material when it is the core of an optical fibre. *(2)*

Total 30 marks

23   Laser measurement of speed

There are many industries where the speed of a gas or a liquid passing through a pipe needs to be measured, and many examples in research where the speed of a fluid moving in a wind tunnel or test tank is needed. Some solid materials, such as cement, grain and powdered coal are moved around by blowing them through pipes using gas, and here too the speed must be measured.

Laser light is used in two distinct ways to measure the speed of flow in such situations. Both methods rely on the light being reflected from small particles carried along with the flow, so they are obviously suitable for the transport of powdered materials, but in other cases particles may have to be added to the fluid.

One of the methods uses a simple interference technique. The laser beam passes through two small slits in an opaque screen, and the two spreading beams shine into the flow, where they overlap. Alternate light and dark bands of light are formed (Young's fringes) and as particles of solid carried along with the flow pass through these bands they scatter light into a detector. The detector therefore picks up flashes of light at a frequency that depends on the spacing of the bands and the speed of flow. The spacing of the bands can be measured directly, or can be worked out from the dimensions of the apparatus, and so the speed can be determined.

The other method uses the Doppler effect; light scattered from moving particles will have its frequency changed by an amount depending on the speed of the particles. The basis of the method is shown in the diagram.

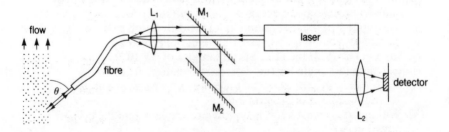

The narrow beam from the laser passes through a small hole in the first mirror, M_1, and is focused by lens L_1 onto the end of the optical fibre. Some of the light is reflected back and some travels down the fibre. When the light travelling down the fibre shines onto the moving particles in the fluid flow, some of it is also reflected back into the fibre (with its changed frequency) and emerges to mix with the original light reflected off the end of the fibre. This combined light reflects off M_1, then M_2, and is focused onto the detector by lens L_2. Because the combined light contains two slightly different frequencies, the light waves will progressively come into step and get out of step, and so the light detected will vary in brightness at this 'beat frequency' which is given by the following equation:

$$\text{beat frequency} = f' - f = \frac{fv \cos \theta}{c}$$

where f is the frequency of the laser light, f' is the frequency of the light reflected off the moving particles, v is the speed of the particles, θ is the angle shown in the diagram, and c is the speed of light, $3 \times 10^8 \, \text{ms}^{-1}$ (For a derivation of this see question 17, 'Radar speed trap'.)

(a) To measure the speed of liquid flow the particles introduced should ideally have the same density as the liquid. Explain the disadvantages of less dense and more dense particles. *(4)*

First method:
(b) Explain why the laser light passing through the two slits
  (i) spreads and overlaps, and
  (ii) produces light and dark bands. *(4)*

(c) Each slit in the screen has a width of 0.05 mm, and their separation is 0.3 mm. The wavelength of the laser light is 600 nm. The transparent pipe carrying a flowing gas/particle mix is 1 m from the screen. Calculate the spacing of the bands of light, and sketch the variation in brightness across the pattern. (Remember that the *extent* of the bands is governed by the diffraction pattern from a *single* slit.) *(6)*

(d) If the detector picks up light flashes at a frequency of 5 kHz, calculate the speed of flow. *(4)*

(e) Explain why this method of measuring speed will work if there are only a *few* particles in the gas stream, but will become confused if there are very many particles. *(2)*

Second method:
(f) Why does the angle θ appear in the calculation of the beat frequency? *(2)*

(g) The same type of laser is used as in the first method. Calculate the frequency of the light. *(2)*

(h) If the detector picks up a beat frequency of 1.2 MHz, and the angle θ is 45°, calculate the speed of flow. *(4)*

(i) Explain one way in which this method will work *better* if many particles are carried by the gas flow. *(2)*

Total 30 marks

24   Diffraction bifocal contact lenses

As people get older, the crystalline lens in the eye becomes less flexible. This means 'reading spectacles' may be needed, and if the person in question wears spectacles, 'bifocal' spectacles may be used. Bifocal contact lenses are a possibility, but until recently have not been very saitsfactory.

There is now a new type of lens available which is much more successful. The back surface of the lens has a series of circular 'zones' etched onto it, and as the light comes through the lens the zones diffract it in different directions, in very much the same way as a diffraction grating. However, unlike the slits in a diffraction grating, the zones are not equally spaced; they are closer together the further they are from the centre, as shown in figure 1.

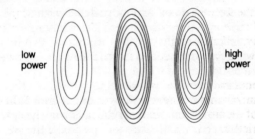

low power   high power

Figure 1

There are ridges on the back surface of the lens, but these are too small to scratch the cornea, and in any case contact lenses are normally fitted with a small clearance from the cornea at the centre. A section through part of the lens is shown in figure 2. It is magnified almost 200 times, and the ridges have been exaggerated to make them noticeable!

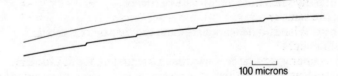

100 microns

Figure 2

Figure 3 compares the action of a normal diffraction grating with a grating made of zones of the type used in the contact lens, except that they are equally spaced. The lens on its own, without the zones, helps the wearer's eye to focus parallel light onto the retina, and so produce clear distance vision.

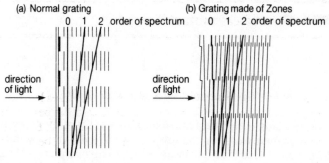

Figure 3

With the zones included, the light in the zero order spectrum still goes in the same direction, so distance vision is still clear. The light in the first order spectrum is bent more than it would be by the lens alone and so comes to a focus in front of the retina: the image produced on the retina is out of focus and is ignored by the brain in comparison with the in focus zero order image.

(a) How does the diffraction of light vary as the width of the slit through which it is passing decreases? Use your answer to explain why, in figure 1.
  (i) narrower zones are needed to produce a more powerful 'extra lens'
  (ii) the zones are narrower at the edge. *(6)*

(b) The diagram of a normal diffraction grating (figure 3a) shows the shape of the wavefronts coming through the slits as if they simply carried straight on. Sketch your own diagram, showing just a few slits, on which the wave fronts are more realistically drawn. (There are *two* important differences.) *(4)*

(c) Compare the brightness of the light passing through gratings of the types shown in figures 3a and 3b. *(2)*

(d) Why are the wave fronts in figure 3b at an angle? *(2)*

(e) Estimate the spacing of the zones from figure 2, and use it to calculate the angle of the first order spectrum. Assume the zones are equally spaced, and behave like a normal diffraction grating with the same spacing, and use a wavelength for green light of 550 nm. What difference will it make if you consider red light and blue light? *(8)*

(f) The last paragraph of the passage explains how the bifocal lens gives a clear image for distance vision. Write a similar paragraph which explains how the lens gives a clear image for close vision. You should make it clear which order of diffracted light is being used, and what happens to the light from a distance which is being ignored. *(8)*

Total 30 marks

25 Baffled!

Adapted from an article in Punch by Keith Waterhouse.

'I was never taught electricity at school, nor was it often a topic of dinner-table conversation among my parents. What I know about the subject I have mastered the hard way. I picked up one piece of electrical knowledge in 1951, while working as a drama critic on the *Yorkshire Evening Post*. Wanting to imply that a certain actress had given a muted performance, I wrote that while undoubtedly she had an electric presence, on this occasion it was as if the electricity had been immersed in water. A kindly sub-editor explained to me that when electricity gets wet, by some miracle of the elements it intensifies rather than diminishes. I have never seen the sense of this, but I conceded the point and have used only gas-driven metaphor since that date.

What with having perforce to change a light bulb here and tune a transistor radio there, I have picked up a pretty sound working knowledge of electrical matters. It is not comprehensive, but when I jot down a summary of what I have learned, I marvel that I have never been asked to write for the *Electrical Journal*:

1. Most electricity is manufactured in power stations where it is fed into wires.

2. Some electricity, however, does not need to go along wires. That used in portable radios for example, and that used in lightning. This kind of electricity is not generated but is just lying around in the air, loose.

3. Electricity becomes intensified when wet. Electric kettles are immune to this.

4. Electricity has to be earthed. That is to say, it has to be connected with the ground before it can function.

5. Electricity makes a low humming noise. This noise may be pitched at different levels for use in doorbells, telephones, etc.

6. Although electricity does not leak out of an empty light socket, that light socket is nevertheless live if you happen to shove your finger in it when the switch is in the 'on' position. So, if it is not leaking, what else is it doing?

7. Electricity is made up of two ingredients, negative and positive. One ingredient travels along a wire covered with blue plastic, and the other along a wire covered with brown plastic. Washing machines need stronger electricity, and for this a booster ingredient is required. This travels along a wire covered in green and yellow plastic.'

(a) A power station does not 'manufacture' electricity, in the sense that the electrons are already there. Describe a simple laboratory experiment which illustrates the principle by which the energy transferred in a power station forces these electrons to move. *(3)*

(b) Give two situations where an electric current is *not* carried by electrons. *(2)*

(c) A portable radio uses batteries for its electricity supply, but also collects some of its 'electricity' out of the air in the form of electromagnetic waves. Explain how a radio transfers the energy associated with electromagnetic waves to the electrons in an electric current using
   (i) a vertical metal rod aerial
   (ii) a horizontal magnetic aerial, consisting of a coil of wire wrapped round a rod of magnetic material (i.e. a ferrite rod aerial). Also explain why this magnetic aerial gives best reception when its axis is *not* pointing towards the radio transmitter. *(6)*

(d) 'Electricity becomes intensified when wet.' Explain why there are no power points in a bathroom (except perhaps a shaver socket), and why the light switch is on the ceiling and is operated by a cord. *(3)*

(e) Mr Waterhouse would probably be astonished to learn that earthing is *not* essential to the operating of any electrical appliance; in fact there is hardly ever any electric current in the earth wire! Explain why the earth wire is there in some electrical appliances, like electric kettles and washing machines. Also explain why a modern hair dryer is probably not earthed. *(4)*

(f) Many electrical appliances *do* make a low humming sound, particularly if they contain a transformer. This is caused by 'magnetostriction'; a piece of iron gets very slightly longer when it is magnetised. Use this information to explain why a transformer hums at 100 Hz (assuming that the frequency of the alternating current is 50 Hz). *(4)*

(g) Shoving your finger in a light socket when it is turned on could be fatal! An electric shock is caused by current flowing through the body, making the muscles contract. Explain why a 5000 V power supply used in a school laboratory can only give a mild shock, the 240 V mains can be fatal, and a car battery, which can supply 200 A to start a car, is not likely to give any shock at all. *(5)*

(h) Explain why the terms 'positive' and 'negative' are totally inappropriate to describe the function of the brown and blue wires in the lead connecting a washing machine to the mains, and state the true purpose of the green and yellow wire. *(3)*

Total 30 marks

26   Maximum power transfer

If you wish to get the maximum power transfer from, say a battery to an electrical appliance, what sort of resistance should the appliance have? At first sight a small resistance seems sensible, because then a large current will flow, but unfortunately drawing a large current from a supply lowers its voltage because of the supply's internal resistance. In the extreme case of zero resistance, a very large current may flow, but all the power transferred heats up the supply! At the other extreme, a large resistance means little current and so only small power transfer. Figure 1 shows a power supply of emf E and internal resistance R_I connected to a load, resistance R_L. It can be shown that the maximum power is transferred when $R_I = R_L$. It is not always possible to design an electrical device to have the same resistance as the supply, but in the case of an a.c. supply, matching can be provided by a transformer. Examples include matching the output resistance of an audio amplifier to that of the loudspeakers, and matching the internal resitance of arc welding equipment to the 'load' which is the very low resistance of the molten metal. Ignoring the real, but small inefficiencies of a transformer, the load resistance R_L matches an effective supply resistance of $N^2 R_L$, where N is the ratio of turns on the primary coil to turns on the secondary coil of the transformer. The details are shown in figure 2.

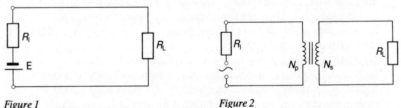

Figure 1   *Figure 2*

The same sort of considerations apply in other situations as well as electrical. Consider the sport of archery; a long bow has a relatively low 'resistance', in this case defined as force/movement, or stiffness, and so fires light arrows most effectively. A cross bow on the other hand is much stiffer, and so the bolts are more massive. It is also possible to use some sort of mechanical 'transformer' to match a power source to the job it has to do. Using a car jack matches the low resistance power supply (the person) to a high resistance job (lifting the car), whereas flippers for underwater swimmers act the other way round by having a stiffness intermediate between that of the legs and that of the water. The anti-reflection coating on camera lenses is yet another example of a 'transformer', this time for light. The coating is ¼ of a wavelength of light thick, and is made of material with a refractive index intermediate between that of the air and that of the glass of the lens. If the air has a refractive index of n_1 and the glass n_2 then the anti-reflection coating should have a refractive index of $\sqrt{n_1 n_2}$, very little light is reflected and the maximum is transmitted through the lens. Figure 3 shows a cross-section through the coated lens surface.

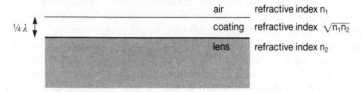

air — refractive index n_1

coating — refractive index $\sqrt{n_1 n_2}$

lens — refractive index n_2

¼ λ

Figure 3

(a) Write down an expression for the current in the circuit of figure 1. (2)

(b) Show that the power delivered to the load is

$$\frac{E^2 R_L}{(R_L + R_L)^2}$$

(2)

(c) EITHER (if you are not confident about calculus)
use $E = 12$ V, $R_I = 3\,\Omega$ to calculate the power delivered for values of R_L of 1, 2, 3, 4, and 5 Ω, and hence show that the power is a maximum if $R_L = R_I$,
OR (if your calculus is good)
show that in general maximum power is delivered if $R_L = R_I$. (6)

(d) What are the causes of the inefficiencies of a transformer? (4)

(e) In low power applications like linking one stage of an audio amplifier to the next, air-cored transformers are used, because iron-cored ones cause distortion. By considering the magnetic properties of iron explain this distortion. (3)

(f) Assuming that a transformer is 100% efficient, write down expressions for the voltage ratio, V_P/V_S and the current ratio, I_P/I_S in terms of N. (p refers to primary and s to secondary circuits). (4)

(g) Use the expressions in (f) to show that the ratio of the supply to load resistances is N^2. (3)

(h) Consider the light reflected off the front surface of the coating on a lens, and that reflected off the lens itself. Why do these combine to give practically no reflected light? (2)

(i) Why does the coating not work perfectly for all colours, and for light coming from all directions? (4)

Total 30 marks

27 Strain gauge

A strain gauge is a piece of electrical resistance wire whose resistance
changes as it is stretched, partly because it gets longer and partly
because it gets thinner. A long thin wire would show larger changes in
length when stretched than a short thick one, for the same force, but a
single length of such wire would be inconvenient. A typical strain gauge
may be made by depositing a thin film of metal (constantan is often
used) on a thin sheet of plastic, and then etching some of the metal away
to leave the shape shown in figure 1. The plastic sheet can now be stuck
onto, say, a girder in a bridge, and as the girder stretches or is
compressed by loads crossing the bridge, the resistances of the strain
gauge varies and can be measured.

Figure 2 shows a metal ring which can be bolted across a crack in the
masonry of an old cathedral. Four strain gauges are attached in the
position shown, and if the crack opens up (or closes) their resistances
will change.

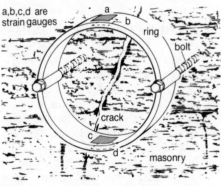

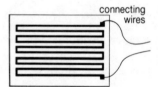

Figure 1 *Figure 2*

Figure 3 shows a typical 'load cell' as used in the electronic scales at
the check out in a supermarket. It consists of an aluminium alloy block
machined to the shape shown, with two strain gauges attached to each of
the central arms.

The electrical measurements are made using a Wheatstone bridge
network, shown in figure 4. When no forces are applied to any of the
strain gauges, their resistances are the same, and the bridge is said to be
balanced. Although there is a potential difference between A and D and
current through the bridge, there is no p.d. across BC. If the resistances
now change the bridge could become unbalanced. For small changes,
the p.d. across BC is proportional to the change of resistance, which is
proportional to the strain. This p.d. can be calibrated directly to show
strain, or movement, or weight.

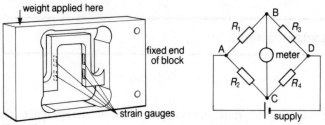

Figure 3   Figure 4

(a) The resistance of a wire length l, radius r and resistivity ρ, is
given by $R = \rho l / \pi r^2$. Using δR, δl and δr for changes in R, l and
r, show that

$$\delta R = \frac{\rho}{\pi}\left(\frac{r\delta l - 2l\delta r}{r^3}\right)$$

(assume $\delta r \ll r$, so that $(\delta r)^2$ can be neglected by comparison with
r^2 and $2r^2\delta r$ can be neglected by comparison with r^3). (4)

(b) Divide the answer to (a) by R to show that

$$\frac{\delta R}{R} = \frac{\delta l}{l} - \frac{2\delta r}{r}$$ (2)

(c) For constantan the ratio

$$\left(\frac{-\delta r/r}{\delta l/l}\right)$$

is constant and equal to approximately ⅓. Show that

$$\frac{\delta R}{R} = \frac{5}{3}\left(\frac{\delta l}{l}\right)$$ (2)

(d) Explain the choice of shape for the etched constantan film
shown in figure 1. In what direction is the strain applied? (3)

(e) If the crack opens up (figure 2), explain which strain gauges
increase in resistance and which decrease. (4)

(f) As a weight is applied to the left hand end of the load cell, which
pair of strain gauges stretches and which is compressed? (3)

(g) For a balanced bridge there is no potential difference between B
and C, and no current through the meter. Use this information
to show that

$$\frac{R_1}{R_3} = \frac{R_2}{R_4}$$ (4)

(h) In the crack monitor the four resistors are all strain gauges. They
are arranged in pairs in the bridge to get the maximum output,
i.e. to make the two sides of the equation in (g) as unequal as
possible when the strain gauges alter. How should a, b, c and d
be related to R_1, R_2, R_3 and R_4? (4)

(i) In a load cell the four resistors in the bridge are also strain
gauges. If the resistance of each of the strain gauges altered with
temperature, why would this *not* affect the balance of the bridge? (2)

(j) How might the output of a load cell be altered by temperature
changes in spite of the statement in (i)? (2)

Total 30 marks

49

Frequency-modulated (FM) radio transmission uses radio waves of very high frequency, for example 100 MHz. In fact the tuned circuit of a radio picks up a small *range* of frequencies, and this range is called the band width. A band width of about 60 kHz is only a tiny fraction of the radio frequency being used, but it allows a lot of information to be contained in the radio signal. For instance, stereo signals can be sent. The pattern of these stereo signals is shown in figure 1. This would be transmitted superimposed on, or 'modulating' the 100 MHz carrier wave, but is shown after it has been 'demodulated'.

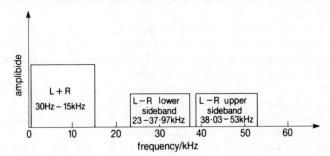

Figure 1

All the speech and music which is being transmitted is contained in the frequency range 30 Hz to 15 kHz, and a mono radio receiver simply uses this part of the signal, which is the right and left speaker information combined, and cuts out the higher frequencies. A stereo radio also uses the higher frequency 'sidebands' which both contain the *difference* between the left and right speaker signals (L–R). These together with the combined L+R signal can be used to produce each of the left and right signals on its own, which after amplification can be used to operate the two speakers separately, so giving the full stereo effect.

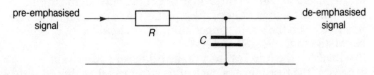

Figure 2

The cutting off of the higher frequencies in the mono radio is done very simply by a capacitor-resistor combination shown in figure 2. As well as cutting off the unwanted sidebands, this also cuts down the amplitude of the required high frequencies in the L+R part of the signal. This does not in fact produce a distorted sound, because the high frequencies are increased in amplitude at the transmitter (called 'pre-emphasis'), so that their reduction ('de-emphasis') by the capacitor-resistor combination reduces them to their *correct* level. This apparently self-cancelling system actually improves the quality of the sound. No radio transmission is perfect: all include unwanted 'noise' and, in the case of FM, the noise picked up during transmission tends to be of high frequency.

(a) In all radio transmission, the sound signal is used to 'modulate' the radio wave in some way. Draw two sketches of waves to show the difference between frequency modulation (FM) and amplitude modulation (AM). *(4)*

(b) The resonant frequency f of a radio's tuned circuit is given by: $f = 1/(2\pi\sqrt{LC})$ where L is inductance and C is capacitance. For the station mentioned in the passage, calculate the inductance if C is 1 pF. *(2)*

(c) The tuned circuit responds to frequencies near the resonant frequency, not just at that one frequency. (This gives the band width referred to in the passage.) Explain why FM would not be possible at all unless this was the case. *(4)*

(d) The 'stereo decoder' part of the radio *adds* one of the sideband (L−R) signals to the L+R signal, and *subtracts* the other sideband signal from the L+R signal. Show that this produces respectively an *all left* signal and an *all right* signal. *(6)*

(e) Explain qualitatively how the C–R combination reduces the amplitude of high frequencies. *(4)*

(f) Why must the de-emphasis in a stereo radio be placed *after* the stereo decoder? *(2)*

(g) The time constant, CR, of the de-emphasis circuit is 50 μs. Show that $C \times R$ has the dimensions of time, and that $R = 4.3$ kΩ and $C = 12$ nF will give approximately the right value. *(4)*

(h) Explain in your own words how the pre-emphasis and de-emphasis of the high frequencies leads to better sound quality. *(4)*

Total 30 marks

29   Overhead power cables

The fact that overhead cables in the National Grid system use very high voltages (400 000 V in the 'super-grid') is well known to physics students, but some other aspects of the design of the grid are less well known. The cables themselves could be made of copper, aluminium or steel, whose densities, resitivities and Young moduli are given in the table.

Material	Young's Modulus/ GNm^{-2}	density/ $10^3\ kgm^{-3}$	resistivity/ $10^{-8}\ \Omega m$
Aluminium	70.3	2.7	2.7
Copper	130	8.9	1.7
Steel	212	7.9	20

In fact, aluminium cables with a steel core are used, as shown in figure 1. These cables are then commonly grouped in fours (a 'quad'), with supporting crosses to keep them correctly spaced. These crosses may further have a large mass attached underneath to keep the four cables properly aligned, see figure 2.

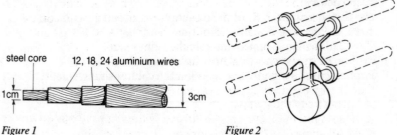

Figure 1

Figure 2

Near each suspension point, each individual cable has a Stockbridge damper attached, as shown in figure 3. The purpose of the dampers is to cut down vibrations of the cables by absorbing energy from them. The cables are suspended from pylons by glass or ceramic insulators, which have to be strong enough to support the weight of the cables. Two sets of insulators in parallel are used to support a quad of cables, but the arrangement has to be rather different where the grid changes direction. This is shown in figure 4. If the change of direction is large, the pylon at the corner will not be a standard one, but will have a heavier and more rigid construction.

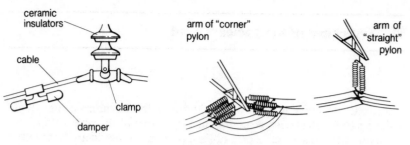

ceramic insulators

cable

clamp

damper

Figure 3

arm of "corner" pylon

arm of "straight" pylon

Figure 4

(a) Calculate the resistance and mass of a 1 m length of the composite cable shown in figure 1. (4)

(b) Calculate the diameter and mass per metre of a copper cable which would have the same resistance. (4)

(c) Since the wires in (a) and (b) have the same resistance, the same energy would be wasted when the same current passed through. Which of the wires would be hottest, and why? (2)

(d) Suggest reasons why four wires are used together, rather than a single thicker wire with the same resistance. (2)

(e) Why is the composite cable used, rather than one of just aluminium, which would have a lower resistance for the same diameter? (2)

(f) As the cables sway in the wind, the 'quad' of wires may tilt. This means that the air flow over it is uneven, and this may make the swaying worse. How does the design of the cross member holding the wires minimise this effect? (1)

(g) Explain why the Stockbridge damper should have a frequency of oscillation similar to that of the cables, and why it should contain moving parts with considerable friction between them. (4)

(h) If the pylons are 250 m apart, calculate the weight which must be supported by the two insulators holding a 'quad'. (2)

(i) Explain carefully why the tension in the cables is much more than their weight, and becomes even greater the less the cables sag in between the pylons. (4)

(j) If the grid direction changes by 30° at a pylon, and the cables make an angle of 20° with the horizontal, calculate the *horizontal* force in the pylon needed to hold a quad of wires with the weight calculated in (h). (4)

(k) Why does the pylon used at a change of direction need to be more substantial than one used on a straight part of the grid? (1)

Total 30 marks

Switching off a current in a low voltage circuit used in schools for teaching about electricity is simple; just undo one of the wires! If the engineers wish to turn off a part of the grid system, because of a fault or for routine maintenance, the problem is considerable since the voltage is so high and the current may be thousands of amperes. The diagrams show a device called an interrupter, used for switching off the 132 kV grid, in its closed and open positions.

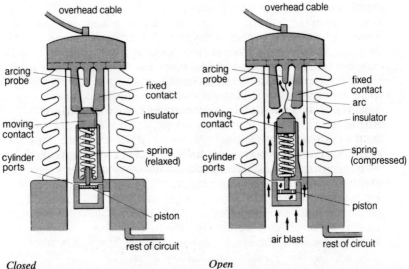

Closed   *Open*

When the contacts are closed and current is flowing, there is very little potential difference across the contact surfaces. The interrupter is operated by releasing an air blast into the space inside it. The pressure on the piston and on the top surface of the moving contact pushes the contact down against the spring, separating the contact surfaces. As they move apart, the resistance between the contacts suddenly increases, so the p.d. also increases. The interruption of the current also has an inductive effect; a large p.d. is induced across the gap and this is in such a direction as to keep the current flowing. These large voltages across a small gap create a very strong field which accelerates any stray ions present.

The ions collide with molecules in the air and cause more ions in a sudden avalanche effect. The air is now highly conducting and the current, called an arc, can flow through it. Since there is a massive transfer of energy in the arc it can cause a lot of damage, and should be extinguished as quickly as possible. The flow of air from the blast extinguishes the arc fairly quickly and dissipates the energy harmlessly.

Now that the current has been turned off a much simpler make/break switch can also be turned off, without causing an arc. This is necessary because small holes in the piston allow the air pressure to equalize gradually and the spring to return the contact to its closed position, but the current must not come back on. The arrangement provides damping to stop the moving contact from oscillating, so that it moves smoothly down when the air blast is let in, and then slowly returns. If it were to bounce up and down the arc would continue for much longer.

(a) Explain what is meant by 'The interruption of the current also has an inductive effect'. Where does the energy come from to generate the voltage, and why is it in such a direction as to keep the current flowing? (6)

(b) What is an ion? (2)

(c) Explain why there are always stray ions present in air. (4)

(d) Describe the ionisation process in more detail, and hence explain what is meant by an avalanche effect. (4)

(e) Part of the energy in the arc heats the air, and part of it heats the metal so much that it may burn and melt (an effect used in arc welding). Notice that the arc is *not* between the closest surfaces. Why is this a deliberate part of the design, and how does the rapid air flow achieve it? (4)

(f) Why is the moving contact potentially an oscillating system? If the moving mass, m, is 20 kg and the stiffness of the spring k, is 8000 Nm^{-1}, calculate the frequency, f, of oscillation.

$$\left(f = \frac{1}{2\pi} \sqrt{\frac{k}{m}} \right)$$ (4)

(g) Sketch graphs of the amplitude against time for an oscillating system which is (i) lightly and (ii) heavily damped. (6)

Total 30 marks

31 Electrical power distribution; ac or dc?

Electrical power distribution in Britain uses a.c. The main reason for this is that a.c. can be transformed easily and efficiently to different voltages, and the higher the voltage used, the less energy is wasted heating the cables. However, d.c. transmission requires thinner wires than a.c. The diagram shows a very simplified three phase a.c. supply system (which is normal in Britain) compared with a d.c. supply. The coils represent the coils of the generator.

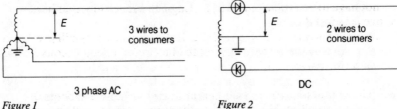

3 phase AC

DC

Figure 1   *Figure 2*

E is the *maximum* potential difference between any cable and earth, and as this is limited by the insulation it is the same for both systems. The *rms* current in the a.c. system is I_a, so the power delivered by the three wires is $\dfrac{3EI_a}{\sqrt{2}} \cos \phi$. ($\phi$ is the phase difference between the current and voltage.) The current in the d.c. system is I_d, so the power delivered by the two wires is $2EI_d$. If the power delivered by each system is to be the same, it can be shown that the resistance of the a.c. wires must be ¾ $\cos^2 \phi$ times that of the d.c. wires. As this is always less than ¾ they must be thicker and more expensive.

Another disadvantage of a.c. is that the current produces oscillating electric and magnetic fields, and so the energy can be thought of as being carried by an electromagnetic wave. As the frequency is only 50 Hz, the wavelength is very long, but for very long distance transmission, say in the USA or Russia, there can be a significant phase difference between different parts of the system.

Although overhead cables are cheaper, in built up areas and in the power link from England to France, underground or undersea cables are necessary. Since damp earth and sea water are electrical conductors, the cable is separated from them by insulation. This causes considerable heating problems, but also means that the cable has a large capacitance. With an a.c. supply, this capacitance must be charged up and discharged 50 times each second, and the current to do this has to be generated, and it has to flow through the cables, even though it does not supply any energy to the consumer.

For two wires, radius a, distance d apart ($d \gg a$, as in overhead cables), the capacitance per metre is given by:

$$C = \frac{\pi \varepsilon_o}{\ln (d/a)}$$

but for an undersea cable radius a, surrounded by insulation radius b, the capacitance per metre is:

$$C = \frac{2\pi \varepsilon_o \varepsilon_r}{\ln (b/a)}$$

Using d.c. means that the capacitance of the wires is irrelevant, except when the current is first switched on.

Yet another advantage of d.c. is that generators in different systems do not have to be synchronised. The English–French link mentioned above is in fact d.c.

In spite of all the advantages of d.c. listed above, a.c. is still preferred because of its 'transformability' and the fact that d.c. to a.c. converters are very expensive.

(a) The output of a power station is at 22 000 V, but the supergrid operates at 400 000 V. Calculate the turns ratio needed on the transformer that makes this change, and by what factor the energy lost in heating the cables is reduced by using the higher voltage. (Assume that the same power is delivered, and the wires are of the same resistance in each case.) *(6)*

(b) Why is there a factor of $\sqrt{2}$ in the calculation in line 11? *(2)*

(c) By equating the expressions given for the power delivered in the a.c. and d.c. cases, and then by equating the power losses in heating the cables, show that the ratio of resistances is as stated in line 15. *(5)*

(d) From your answer to (c), show that the cost of the cables for the a.c. system is $2/\cos^2 \phi$ times that for d.c. *(4)*

(e) Calculate the wavelength of a 50 Hz electromagnetic wave. How far away from the generator will the current have a phase difference of 90°? (Speed of em waves $= 3 \times 10^8 \text{ ms}^{-1}$.) *(4)*

(f) Show that the capacitance of a pair of parallel wires in an overhead transmission system is small compared with that of an undersea cable. Take the radius of the wires as 1.5 cm, their separation as 2 m, and the radius of the insulation on the undersea cable as 2.5 cm. $\varepsilon_o = 8.85 \times 10^{-12} \text{ Fm}^{-1}$ and $\varepsilon_r = 3$. *(4)*

(g) The passage says that the charging and discharging of the capacitance does not provide any energy for the consumer. What *does* happen to the energy involved? *(5)*

Total 30 marks

Beams of electrons are used to produce the picture on a television
screen, and on the screens of oscilloscopes. They are also used to
remove minute pieces of material to make microchips, in electron
crystallography and in electron microscopes. For all these, very precise
control of the direction of the electron beam is necessary; a colour
television picture can only look sharp if the dots of phosphor made to
glow by the electron beam are very small. The paths of the electrons are
controlled by 'electron lenses', which may use electric fields or magnetic
fields to guide them. Fields are created by using cylinders at different
potentials as in figure 1, and their shapes are usually quite complex, so
they are plotted experimentally by measuring the equipotentials.

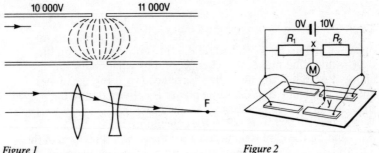

Figure 1   *Figure 2*

Figure 2 shows a simple apparatus for doing this. The base sheet is made
of conducting paper (but with quite a high resistance), and the pieces of
metal firmly clamped down on it represent a cross section along the axis
of two cylinders. A potential difference is applied between the
'cylinders', and this p.d. is also divided up in a known ratio by R_1 and
R_2. The probe Y is placed on the paper and moved around to find all the
places where the meter reads zero, so that X and Y are at the same
potential. New values for R_1 and R_2 are chosen, and another
equipotential plotted. Figure 1 shows the equipotentials for this
situation, and the equivalent combination of glass lenses for light. The
electron lens accelerates the electrons and it also has a focussing effect.
In an electron gun in a television tube the arrangement is a little more
complex, but basically similar. Slight variation of the potential
difference allows the focus of the electron beam to be adjusted so that it
is on the screen.

Data: charge on electron $= 1.6 \times 10^{-19}$ C
mass of electron $= 9.1 \times 10^{-31}$ kg
acceleration due to gravity $= 9.8 \, \text{ms}^{-2}$

(a) In the simulation experiment to plot the equipotentials, the p.d. used is 10 V and $R_1 = R_2$. Which equipotential will be plotted, and where on the paper should Y be placed? *(4)*

(b) If $R_1 = 100 \, \Omega$, what value should R_2 have to plot the 2 V equipotential? *(3)*

(c) On a copy of the equipotentials shown in figure 2, sketch in the shape of the field lines and show their direction. *(4)*

(d) At any point in the field, in which direction will the force be on an electron? *(2)*

(e) For an electron travelling from left to right, and starting above the axis of the lens, explain why
  (i) it is accelerated
  (ii) its path is bent towards the axis
  (iii) it is then bent back again. *(6)*

(f) To get the focusing effect, the 'converging lens' part of the field must be more powerful (i.e. produce more bending) than the 'diverging lens' part of the field. (Compare with the light equivalent.) Give *two* reasons why the electron path is converged more than it is diverged, in spite of the symmetry of the field. *(4)*

(g) If the first cylinder is at a potential of 10 000 V and the second one at 11 000 V, both with respect to the cathode which emits the electrons, calculate the final speed of the electrons. (Ignore any relativistic mass increase.) *(3)*

(h) Calculate the time taken for an electron travelling at this speed to reach a screen 30 cm away from the electron lens, and show that the distance it falls due to gravity, during this time, is negligible. *(4)*

Total 30 marks

33 Coulomb explosion imaging

The shape of a molecule is an important property. It has a bearing on how molecules pack together to form a solid material, and on how various biological processes work. Finding the shape has normally been done by using X-ray or electron scattering and interference, but these can only really tell how the molecules pack together, and so can only be used for materials which can be crystallised. Then the individual shapes of the molecules have to be inferred from this information.

An entirely different approach has now been developed in Israel and the United States. A collection of the molecules to be analysed is first ionised, and then accelerated to a high speed, maybe as high as 1/50 of the speed of light. The resulting beam is neutralised, and then smashed into a foil of solid material about 30 atoms thick. The chances of the nuclei of the molecules in the beam colliding directly with nuclei in the foil are extremely remote, but the interaction of the electrons is sufficient to strip the valence electrons off each of the atoms in the molecule. The 'molecule' now becomes a collection of positive ions and so the bonding is lost, and the ions fly apart because of their mutual repulsion. When the ions reach the detector, they still have their relative positions and so the shape of the original molecule can be determined.

Analysing the record from the detector is, however, not a simple matter. As the molecule approaches the foil, the atoms in it will be vibrating relative to each other. The molecule passes through the foil in a very short time, much shorter than the period of the vibrations, so the ions produced may be at different separations and already moving towards each other or apart, depending on what phase of the vibration they were in when they passed through the foil. Also, there is no way of ensuring that each molecule is in the same orientation as it passes through the foil. The record can therefore only give a probability distribution of the relative positions of the atoms within the molecule.

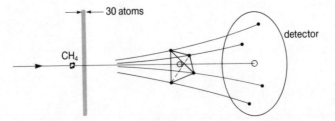

Data: charge on electron $= 1.6 \times 10^{-19}$ C

$$\frac{1}{4\pi\varepsilon_o} = 9 \times 10^9 \, \text{Nm}^2\text{C}^{-2}$$

mass of proton $= 1.67 \times 10^{-27}$ kg
mass of C 12 ion $= 1.99 \times 10^{-26}$ kg
energy to change CH_4 molecule to $C^{4+} + 4H^+ = 3.53 \times 10^{-17}$ J
speed of light $= 3 \times 10^8 \, \text{ms}^{-1}$

(a) Why must the molecules be ionised before they can be
accelerated? (2)
(b) How, in principle, could the acceleration be carried out? (2)
(c) If the nucleus of each atom in the foil is 10^{-14} m across, make a
rough estimate of the probability of a direct collision between a
nucleus in the accelerated molecule and a nucleus in the foil.
You could start by simply considering the cross sectional area of
a nucleus as a fraction of the cross sectional area of an atom, but
you may be able to think of ways of improving on this. (4)
(d) Explain, in energy terms, why the molecule must slow down as it
passes through the foil, even if there is no direct collision. (2)
(e) Using the information given for a methane molecule (CH_4),
originally travelling at $\frac{1}{50}$ of the speed of light, show that this
slowing down is very slight. (4)
(f) Once a molecule of CH_4 has passed through the foil, calculate
the force of repulsion on a H^+ ion from the C^{4+} ion if they are
$\times 10^{-10}$ m apart. (2)
(g) The force in (f) is, of course, not the only force on each ion; the
ions *all* repel each other. The shape of the molecule is a regular
tetrahedron, with a hydrogen atom at each vertex and the
carbon atom in the middle. Why do the forces from the H^+ ions
on the C^{4+} ion cancel out, and why is the force in (f) larger than
the forces from the other H^+ ions? (6)
(h) What happens to the forces of repulsion between the ions as
they travel to the detector? (2)
(i) Say as much as you can about the curvature of the paths of the
ions between the foil and the detector. (2)
(j) Consider two molecules passing through the foil. One happens
to have its electrons removed when a hydrogen atom is at one
extreme of its oscillation, and the other when a hydrogen atom is
at the other extreme of its oscillation. Why is the spread of the
H^+ ions when they reach the detector less than a straightforward
enlargement of the molecule? (4)

Total 30 marks

34 Piezo electric microscope

Some crystals, of which quartz is probably the most well known, have a structure in which no positive charges are located at the centre point of a straight line between two negative charges, or vice-versa, as in figure 1. If an electric field is applied to such a crystal, the structure is distorted and the crystal changes shape and size, as in figure 2. The process also works the other way, in that squeezing or stretching the crystal generates an electric field, and hence a potential difference across the crystal. Such materials are called piezo electric.

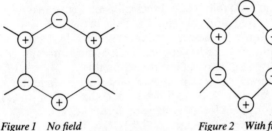

Figure 1 No field   *Figure 2 With field*

Common uses of piezo electric materials are gas lighters that produce a spark when squeezed, and the oscillating quartz crystal which is the time keeper in a quartz watch. However, a new use is in the scanning tunnelling microscope (STM). The limit of resolution, that is the smallest detail that can be seen, of an optical microscope is set by the wavelength of light, which goes down to about 4×10^{-7} m. The STM uses the tiny movements produced by the piezo electric effect to get much better resolution, down to the size of individual atoms! Figure 3 shows the arrangement of a very sharp metal needle which can be moved in any direction by the piezo electric arms x, y.

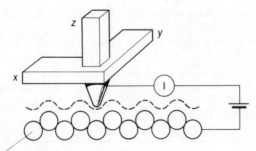

atoms of surface

Figure 3

A small potential difference, say 1 V, is maintained between the needle and the conducting surface of the material to be scanned. When the needle tip and the surface are only a few atomic diameters apart, a small current of electrons, I ($\sim 10^{-9}$ A) flows across the gap by a process known as 'quantum tunnelling'. If the two surfaces are closer, this current rises, and if the surfaces are further apart, the current falls. In fact the current is monitored and kept constant by small movements in the z direction, so that the needle tip follows the atomic contours of the surface (or more correctly follows the variations in electron density). The needle is made to scan across the surface in the x direction, then move very slightly in the y direction and make another scan in the x direction, in the same way that an electron beam scans the face of a TV tube to build up the whole picture. While this scan is going on, the potential differences across the x, y and z piezo electric arms are recorded by a computer, which then has the information to construct a three-dimensional picture of the surface. Remarkable 'pictures' of single molecules have been obtained using this technique, but altering the scanning pattern can also reveal surfaces in *less* detail, so that various magnifications can be used, from the same level as an optical microscope down to atomic level.

(a) On a sketch copy of figure 2 show the direction of electric field which has produced the distortion. (2)

(b) If a piezo electric material is squeezed, explain the energy transfer that takes place to produce the potential difference. (4)

An electric field of 1 Vm^{-1} produces a strain of 5×10^{-10} in a certain piezo electric material. Each of the piezo electric arms is 4 mm long. The size of the atoms being scanned is 3×10^{-10} m.

(c) A potential difference of 0.8 V is applied across the ends of one of the arms.
  (i) Calculate the field strength along the arm.
  (ii) Calculate the strain produced by this field.
  (iii) Calculate change in length of the arm.
  (iv) Can this arrangement pick out atoms? Explain your answer. (8)

(d) An area of 1.2×10^{-9} m by 1.2×10^{-9} m of a surface is to be scanned. Calculate the potential difference across the x arm needed to produce this movement. If the area is covered by 8 scans, sketch graphs of the potential differences across the x, y and z arms against time. Give the potential difference scale on each, and plot them on the same time scale. (14)

(e) How would you alter the scanning pattern to get less detail? (2)

Total 30 marks

Magnetic fields are used in several different ways in metal working industries. One obvious way is that iron and iron-based metals can be held firmly in place while they are machined, by what is known as a magnetic chuck. It would seem that electromagnets would be ideal in such a chuck, because they can be turned off to position the metal to be machined, turned on to grip it, and turned off again to release it once it has been machined. However there is an ingenious version that uses permanent magnets and variable magnetic circuits. A magnetic circuit is analogous to an electrical circuit, with *magnetomotive force*, F_m, being the equivalent of potential difference, *magnetic flux*, Φ, being the equivalent of current, and *reluctance*, $\mathcal{R}$, being the equivalent of resistance. The equation for an electric circuit is $V = IR$. Similarly, for a magnetic circuit, $F_m = \Phi\mathcal{R}$. (In an electromagnet operated by a coil with a current in it F_m is the current $\times$ the number of turns and is called 'current-turns'.) The analogy can be pursued further, with reluctance and resistance being very similar:

$$R = \frac{l}{\sigma A}$$

$$\mathcal{R} = \frac{l}{\mu A}$$

where l is the length of a particular part of the electric or magnetic circuit, A is the cross-sectional area of the material of that part, and σ is the conductivity, μ the permeability of the material. The diagram shows the design and operation of a magnetic chuck used for holding a piece of metal on a grinding machine.

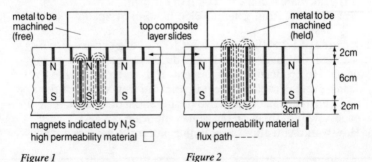

Figure 1

Figure 2

The top composite layer can be slid along by a simple lever into the two positions shown. The magnets are 15 cm deep from front to back. The magnetomotive force from each magnet is 200 A (which is the equivalent of passing a current of 1 A through a coil of 200 turns in an electromagnet).

> Data: The magnetic permeabilities of the various materials are as follows:
>
> | | |
> |---|---|
> | magnet, | $\mu = 6 \times 10^{-4}\,\mathrm{Hm}^{-1}$ |
> | high permeability metal in chuck, | $\mu = 12 \times 10^{-4}\,\mathrm{Hm}^{-1}$ |
> | non-magnetic material in chuck, | |
> | and air, | $\mu = 12 \times 10^{-7}\,\mathrm{Hm}^{-1}$ |
> | metal to be machined, | $\mu = 8 \times 10^{-4}\,\mathrm{Hm}^{-1}$ |

(a) Name one material which has
   (i) a low conductivity
   (ii) a high conductivity
   (iii) a low permeability
   (iv) a high permeability.   (4)
(b) Draw the equivalent electrical circuit for the flux path shown in figure 1. You should indicate what is the equivalent of the magnet and of the pieces of high and low permeability material. (4)
(c) Explain why very little flux exists in the metal to be machined in figure 1, but a significant amount in figure 2.   (4)
(d) Estimate the average length of the flux path in figure 1 (shown by the solid line).   (2)
(e) Estimate the reluctance of the flux path in figure 1. Make the simplifying assumption that the cross-section of the path is the same all the way round.   (6)
(f) For figure 1, estimate the flux produced.   (2)
(g) Give *two* reasons why the flux in figure 2 must be less than that in figure 1.   (4)
(h) Explain why this magnetic chuck will hold the metal to be worked *much less* securely when the base of the metal is not perfectly flat.   (4)

Total 30 marks

The rather curious definition of the ampere is that current which when flowing through two very thin, parallel, very long straight wires one metre apart in a vacuum, produces a force between the wires of 2×10^{-7} N per metre length. The force is ridiculously small to measure at all, and is certainly no use for any industrial process. However as the distance between the wires decreases the force increases in inverse proportion, and if the current in both wires is doubled the force is four times stronger. The force can be large enough to be a serious hazard in some situations, for instance the cylindrical coils used to produce very large magnetic fields for research can be crushed in one direction and explode in another! Such large forces can also be put to positive use in shaping metals. Figure 1 shows the circuit used to obtain a very large current for a short time. Figure 2 shows the approximate variation with time of the current surge through the coil shown in figure 3. Current is induced in the metal pipe, and the repulsion between the two currents forces the metal to bulge into the groove in the collar. The collar is now permanently fixed onto the end of the pipe.

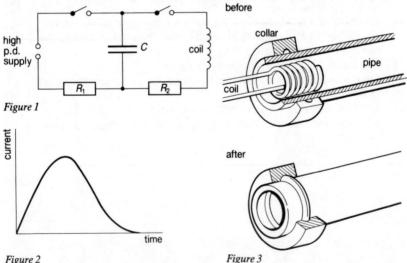

Figure 1

Figure 2

Figure 3

(a) Draw a sketch to show the direction of magnetic field produced by the current through a long straight wire. (3)

(b) Use your answer to (a) and Fleming's left hand rule to work out the direction of the force between the wires in the definition of the ampere if the currents in both wires are in the same direction. (3)

(c) A cylindrical coil or solenoid has a large current in it. By considering where the currents in different parts of the coil are flowing parallel to each other, and where they are flowing in opposite directions, say in which direction the coil will tend to be crushed and in which direction it will tend to explode. *(4)*

(d) Calculate the force per metre between two long parallel wires each carrying a current of 10 000 A if they are 0.5 cm apart in a vacuum. *(4)*

(e) To get a force in the right direction to make the pipe bulge, should the currents in the coil and the pipe be flowing in the same or opposite directions? *(3)*

(f) Copy the sketch of the current/time variation (figure 2) and on the same time scale show the emf induced in the metal pipe. Still on the same time scale, show the approximate variation of *current* induced in the pipe. (Remember that the pipe itself behaves as an inductor, so the current will not be in phase with the emf.) *(6)*

(g) The bank of capacitors should be charged up slowly, so that the current drawn from the supply is not too large, but should be discharged quickly to get a large current for the metal forming. Comment on the values of the resistors R_1 and R_2. *(3)*

(h) The discharge part of the circuit is potentially an oscillating circuit. By considering the energy transfers in the process, explain why there will be practically no oscillation of current. *(4)*

Total 30 marks

Powered ships normally use a propeller system to enable them to move.
The forward force on the ship is provided by giving backward
momentum to the water. Various forms of engine, such as steam
turbines or gas turbines may be used, but they tend to be only about
20% efficient. Whatever type of engine is used, the propeller system is
inefficient, because it is converting circular motion into linear motion;
the large amount of turbulence in the water near a propeller means
energy has been wasted.

A novel means of propulsion may be possible in the near future
thanks to the advances in superconductor technology. Superconductors
will be used to make powerful electromagnets, producing a magnetic
field in the sea water below the ship. At the same time an electric
current will be passed through the sea water from electrodes on the
bottom of the ship's hull. The current is acted on by the field, producing
a force on the water in one direction, and a corresponding force on the
ship in the other, as shown in the diagram.

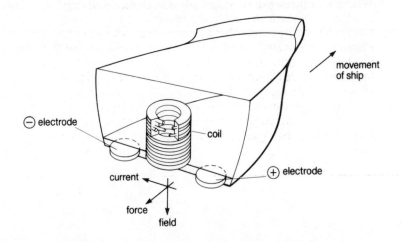

Of course the ship must have some sort of electrical generator, but the
shaft and propeller are no longer needed. What is more, placing
electrodes in various positions on the bottom of the hull and switching
the current to selected pairs of them can produce a force in any
direction, so the ship can be steered. The rudder is therefore
unnecessary too.

As with most advances, there may be a price to pay. The passage of
current will electolyse the sea water, producing potentially harmful

chemical concentrations. Also the large currents created in the sea water will warm the water up though given the vast volume of the sea, the rise in temperature is unlikely to be serious.

(a) If a propeller can make 100 kg of water each second move at $20\ \text{ms}^{-1}$, how much force will it produce? (2)

(b) Why will the force calculated in (a) reduce as the ship gains speed? (2)

(c) What happens to the resistance force (drag) of the ship through the water as it speeds up? Under what conditions does a ship reach its maximum speed? (4)

(d) In the electromagnetic form of propulsion, what are the charge carriers in the sea water? (2)

(e) Sketch the sort of path you would expect the current to follow through the sea water. (3)

(f) Write down an expression for the force on a conductor of length l carrying a current I through a uniform magnetic field strength B. Why is this expression not strictly applicable to the situation shown in the diagram? (4)

(g) For a large ship a large force will be needed, say 2×10^6 N. If the distance between the electrodes is 50 m and the strength of the field is 10 T, calculate the current needed to produce this force. (Assume the expression in (f) is applicable.) (3)

(h) Where would you place the positive and negative electrodes to produce a force which would steer the ship to the left? (3)

(i) Using alternating current between the electrodes would almost eliminate the electrolysis of the sea water, but would also produce no net driving force! Explain why there would be no force, and suggest another change to the system which would allow a.c. to be used effectively. (4)

(j) Electromagnetic machines normally have an iron core to increase the field. Iron saturates in a field of about 2 tesla. Explain why superconducting electromagnets do not have a core. (3)

Total 30 marks

Most of the motors used in household appliances are of the type shown in figure 1. Current is fed to the rotor by carbon brushes and a commutator. This part of the motor is the most likely to go wrong and wear out, therefore needing servicing or replacement. For low power applications, like hair dryers or the pumps in automatic washing machines, an alternative is to use an *induction motor*, figure 2. This type is from a washing machine, and is called a 'shaded pole' motor.

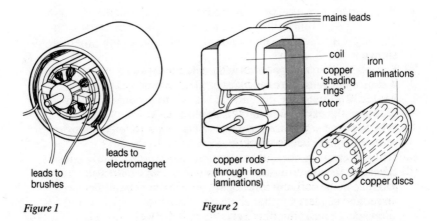

Figure 1   *Figure 2*

The induction motor has thick copper bars at an angle along the edge of a laminated iron cylinder. These bars are short-circuited at their ends by two copper discs. There are no electrical connections to this 'cage' of copper bars and discs, and so the motor has no brushes to wear out, and is much more maintenance-free. Both motors use a coil or coils round laminated iron to produce the magnetic field in which the rotor turns, but the induction motor also has 'shading rings' which are essentially short circuited coils around *part* of the pole pieces. The graphs, figure 3, are for the induction motor. They show the mains voltage applied to the coil, the current that flows through the coil as a result, the magnetic flux produced by this current, the voltage induced across the larger of the shading rings by this changing flux, and the current that flows in the shading ring as a result. This produces its own magnetic flux, and so the total flux is the sum of the two, shown in the final graph. The important thing to notice is that this combined flux comes to a peak *later* than the unaltered flux; it is as if the peak of the flux had moved from the *unshaded* to the *shaded* part of the field in a short time interval.

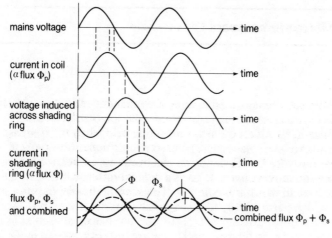

mains voltage

current in coil
(α flux Φ_p)

voltage induced
across shading
ring

current in
shading
ring (α flux Φ)

flux Φ_p, Φ_s
and combined

combined flux $\Phi_p + \Phi_s$

Figure 3

Brushed motor:
(a) Give *two* reasons why the brushes in a motor wear out. (2)
(b) Give *two* reasons why the brushes are made of carbon. (2)
Both types of motor:
(c) Explain why the rotors and the pole pieces are made of iron,
    why they are laminated, and why there must be as small an air
    gap as possible between them. (8)
Induction motor:
(d) There is a phase difference between the mains voltage and the
    current in the coil, but it is *not* 90°, as it would be for a perfect
    inductor. Explain. (2)
(e) Explain carefully the phase relationship between the flux
    produced by the coil and the voltage induced across the shading
    ring. (4)
(f) The flux in which the rotor moves consists of three parts; the
    unshaded part, the part through the large shading ring and the
    part through the large and small shading rings together. The first
    two of these are shown on the final graph. On a sketch copy of
    these two, add the third flux. (4)
(g) Why are currents induced in the copper bars of the rotor, and
    why do these currents make the rotor turn? (4)
(h) Which way does the rotor turn? (2)
(i) In the detailed diagram of the rotor, note that the copper bars
    are not parallel to the axis. Suggest a reason for this. (Hint: the
    shading rings *are* parallel to the axis.) (2)

Total 30 marks

Hand held compasses for navigating are magnetic. The usual design consists of a magnet, in the form of a needle, pivoted at its centre so that it can align itself with the Earth's magnetic field when the compass is held in a horizontal plane. The pivoted needle makes this type of compass fairly fragile. Recently an electronic compass has been made which has no moving parts. It gives a digital reading which tells the user the direction in which it is pointing. The basis of the compass is a small ring of a high permeability ferromagnetic material (that is it is easy to magnetise). Four 'driving' coils, D1 to D4 are placed at regular intervals round the ring, as in figure 1, and these are fed with current in the form of a square wave from a battery operated oscillator at a frequency of 8 kHz. Since the field in the ring is changing, potential differences will be induced across the four 'sensing' coils, S1 to S4. However these are connected in pairs, S1 and S3 and S2 and S4 and in opposite directions, so that if the changes in field are the same all the way round the ring, as in figure 2, the induced potential differences cancel, giving no output.

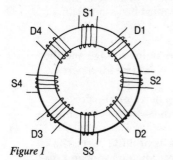

Figure 1

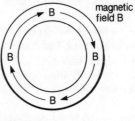

Figure 2

If the ring is placed in an external field, say the Earth's field, there will be a magnetic field in the ring as shown in figure 3.

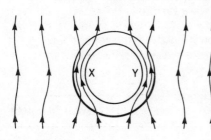

Figure 3

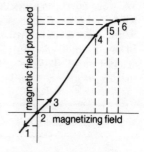

Figure 4

The total field is now the combined effect of figures 2 and 3. If the fields simply added together in a linear fashion, the pairs of sensing coils would still not give any output, because although the fields at X and Y in figure 3 are now different, the *changes* in field caused by the square wave would still be the same. However, magnetic materials do not behave in a linear fashion, but can be magnetically saturated as shown in figure 4. If the currents from the drive coils are chosen to almost produce saturation, adding the Earth's field makes very little difference, but subtracting it *does* make a significant difference. When the current turns off, the Earth's field makes a significant difference in either direction, so the change of field, and hence the rate of change of field, is different in the two sides of the ring. Just how much difference there is, and whether it affects S1 and S3 or S2 and S4, or both, depends on the orientation of the ring with respect to the Earth's field. Hence the output can be electronically processed to give a digital readout of the bearing.

(a) Explain the advantages and disadvantages of the electronic compass compared with the magnetic needle type. *(4)*

(b) The field B in an infinitely long solenoid is $B = \mu IN/L$, where μ is the permeability of the material, N/L is the turns per unit length, and I is the current. Explain why this formula is applicable to the very different situation of the ring, and the meaning of N and L in this context. *(4)*

(c) The 'square' wave of current gives zero current for 5×10^{-5} s, rises to its maximum in 1.25×10^{-5} s, stays at that maximum for 5×10^{-5} s and fails back to zero in 1.25×10^{-5} s. This cycle then repeats. Draw a graph showing this variation with time, and on the same time axis sketch a graph of the induced potential difference across one of the S coils. *(6)*

(d) Why does a magnetic material become saturated? *(4)*

(e) On figure 4, point 1 is the field at Y caused by the external field only, point 2 is produced when there is no external field and no current in the D coils, and point 3 is the field at X caused by the external field only. Point 4 is the combined effect at Y of the external field and the field due to the current in the D coils, and point 5 is the field caused just by the current in the D coils (no external field) and point 6 is the combined effect at X of the external field and the field due to the current in the D coils. On a copy of the graph show that the *changes* of field at X and Y are different as the current switches on and off. *(6)*

(f) Explain why the material of the ring would, or would not be suitable for
   (i) a transformer core
   (ii) the permanent magnet of a loudspeaker
   (iii) the recording head of a tape recorder or a disc drive. *(6)*

Total 30 marks

The first subatomic particles to be discovered were electrons. These have very little mass (about ½₀₀₀ the mass of the lightest atom) and are negatively charged, which makes them easy to accelerate up to high speeds. For instance in a domestic television set the electrons may be accelerated using a potential difference of 11 000 V, which gives them a speed of approximately 62 000 000 ms^{-1}. Since this is a significant fraction of the speed of light, relativistic mechanics must be used for accurate calculations.

To accelerate charged particles to higher energies it is convenient to make them move in circular paths, so that they can be accelerated repeatedly. This is done by making them travel in a magnetic field, and was first put into practice in 1930 by E. Lawrence. His 'cyclotron' had a diameter of 13 cm and accelerated protons to an energy of 80 000 eV. The principle of its construction is shown in the diagrams, figure 1 and figure 2.

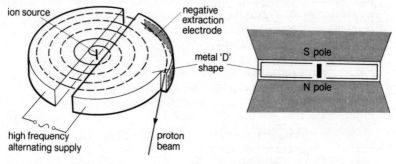

Figure 1   *Figure 2*

At the centre was a source of protons, which would be accelerated to whichever 'D' happened to be negative, then travel in a semicircle to arrive back at the gap when the *other* 'D' was negative. The proton would therefore be accelerated again, and so on, each time travelling in a semicircle of bigger radius. The accelerating voltage was provided by a fixed frequency alternating supply, which was possible since the protons took the same time to travel each semicircle, regardless of its radius.

As higher and higher energies were required relativistic mass increases, even for protons, became significant. One modification was to change the frequency of the alternating voltage as the protons moved to larger radii and higher energies.

Modern particle accelerators are much more complex, with circular paths many kilometres in diameter, variable frequency accelerating sections, and superconducting electromagnets. Particle physicists also accelerate particles and their antiparticles in the same rings, and collide them with each other to get even more energetic collisions than with stationary targets. One proposed machine, a direct descendant of the cyclotron, is the Superconducting Super Collider. It will have a diameter of 26 km and will accelerate protons up to energies of 20 TeV $(20 \times 10^{12} \, \text{eV})$.

Data: charge on electron $= 1.6 \times 10^{-19} \, \text{C}$
1 electron-volt $= 1.6 \times 10^{-19} \, \text{J}$
rest mass of electron $= 9.1 \times 10^{-31} \, \text{kg}$
rest mass of proton $= 1.7 \times 10^{-27} \, \text{kg}$

$$m = \frac{m_o}{\sqrt{1 - (v^2/c^2)}}$$

where m = mass, m_o = rest mass, v = speed and c = speed of light $(3 \times 10^8 \, \text{ms}^{-1})$

(a) Show that the speed of $62\,000\,000 \, \text{ms}^{-1}$ for electrons in a television is correct. (Ignore relativistic effects.) (3)

(b) Using $62\,000\,000 \, \text{ms}^{-1}$ calculate the percentage mass increase from the rest mass of an electron. (3)

(c) The force on a particle charge q moving at speed v in a magnetic field of flux density B is Bqv. In a cyclotron this force produces the centripetal acceleration v^2/r. Show that the time taken for a proton to complete one circle is $2\pi m/Bq$, and so is independent of the radius of the path. (4)

(d) Calculate the speed of a proton with energy $80\,000 \, \text{eV}$, assuming relativistic effects may be neglected. Is the assumption reasonable? (4)

(e) From your working for question (c) derive an expression for B in terms of m, v, q and r, and hence show that Lawrence must have used a flux density of $0.64 \, \text{T}$. (3)

(f) Show that the frequency of the alternating supply to accelerate the protons was $9.5 \, \text{MHz}$. (3)

(g) For a cyclotron to produce higher energy protons, when relativistic effects become significant, does the time for a circuit increase or decrease? How should the frequency of the alternating supply be changed? (4)

(h) Explain why the change of frequency in (g) means that protons will be fired out of the accelerator in bursts at a much lower frequency than $9.5 \, \text{MHz}$. (3)

(i) An antiproton has the same mass as a proton, but opposite charge. How is it possible for protons and antiprotons to be kept in circular paths close to each other by the same magnets? (3)

Total 30 marks

41   Nuclear fusion and its containment

Nuclear fusion is the joining together, or 'fusing', of the nuclei of light atoms to make nuclei of heavier atoms. Since the nuclei of the heavier atoms are more stable, energy is released in the process. Under the right conditions, this could be a considerable amount of energy; for instance it provides the energy radiated in vast amounts by the sun and other stars, and the terrifying destructive power of hydrogen bombs.

There are many possible reactions, but one which is the subject of extensive research for peaceful power production is:

$$\,^2_1H + \,^3_1H \rightarrow \,^4_2He + \,^1_0n + \text{energy}$$

$\,^2_1H$ is an isotope of hydrogen, called deuterium, and occurs naturally in the hydrogen in sea water, though only to the extent of 1 part in 45 000. $\,^3_1H$ is another isotope of hydrogen called tritium. This is too rare to be extracted from natural hydrogen, but can be made by bombarding lithium–6 with neutrons:

$$\,^6_3Li + \,^1_0n \rightarrow \,^3_1H + \,^4_2He + \text{energy}$$

The neutrons to bombard the lithium could be provided by the fusion reaction once it has been started, so the basic fuels would be deuterium and lithium. Enough of these are available to give ample energy for millions of years! Another advantage is that none of the final products is radioactive, although tritum is radioactive, with a half-life of 12.4 years.

Unfortunately there are many very difficult engineering problems to be solved before nuclear fusion can be controlled on a big enough scale to provide useful energy.

The main difficulty is that nuclei of any atoms are positively charged and repel each other very strongly, and so have to be travelling at enormous speeds before they collide strongly enough for the short range 'strong nuclear force' to make them fuse. If the nuclei were at an extremely high temperature, say 100 000 000 K, the collisions between them would cause enough nuclei to fuse to provide enough energy to maintain the high temperature *and* give out useful extra energy. This would be in the form of radiation which could be used, indirectly, to boil water to run steam turbines as in a conventional power station.

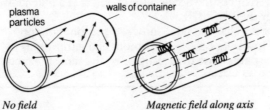

plasma particles

walls of container

No field   *Magnetic field along axis*

At this temperature the gas cannot be contained by any known material! Instead it has to be kept from touching the walls of the container by using a magnetic field. The particles of a gas at this temperature consist of electrons and nuclei separated from each other (properly called a plasma), and these charged particles moving at high speed are deflected by the magnetic field as shown in the diagrams.

Data: charge on electron, $e = 1.6 \times 10^{-19}$ C

$\dfrac{1}{4\pi\varepsilon_o} = 9 \times 10^9$ Nm^2C^{-2}

for nucleus at temperature T, K.E. $\approx kT$

Boltzmann's constant, $k = 1.38 \times 10^{-23}$ JK^{-1}

mass of neutron $= 1.008986$ u (atomic mass unit)

mass of $^2_1$H $= 2.014740$ u

mass of $^3_1$H $= 3.017005$ u

mass of $^4_2$He $= 4.003873$ u

mass of $^6_3$Li $= 6.017034$ u

1 u $= 1.67 \times 10^{-27}$ kg $= 931$ MeV

(a) Why is the equivalent for 1 u expressed in kg *and* MeV?   (2)

(b) By consisting the mass before and after the reactions, calculate the energy released in each of the reactions listed.   (4)

(c) Calculate the force of electrical repulsion between the nuclei in each reaction if they are 10^{-14} m apart. (Force F between two charges q_1 and q_2, distance r apart, is given by

$$F = \frac{1}{4\pi\varepsilon_o}\frac{q_1 q_2}{r^2}\Big)$$ (3)

(d) Estimate the speed of a lithium nucleus at the temperature stated.   (3)

(e) Describe the path taken by a nucleus in the magnetic field if it is travelling

  (i) along the field   (iii) in some direction between

  (ii) perpendicular to the field   the two.   (6)

(f) Calculate the strength of magnetic field needed to keep a lithium nucleus contained within a diameter of 0.2 m. (The force F on a charge q moving at speed v in field B is given by $F = Bqv$, and centripetal acceleration $a = v^2/r$)   (6)

(g) If the plasma is prevented from touching the sides of the containment vessel, why will they still get very hot?   (2)

Total 30 marks

'Tokamac' is the name for a magnetic field system used with nuclear fusion in the JET undertaking. (See question 41.) Part of the action is that of a transformer, with the plasma in its toroidal vacuum chamber acting as the secondary coil. A huge current, of up to seven million amps, can be induced in the plasma for a short time, and it is hoped that this will heat up the plasma to a temperature where the fusion reaction becomes self sustaining, although other methods of heating, such as injecting energetic particles into the plasma, and the use of radio beams, are also employed. The layout of the Tokamac is shown in the diagram below, and the graphs show the currents that have been achieved in the plasma.

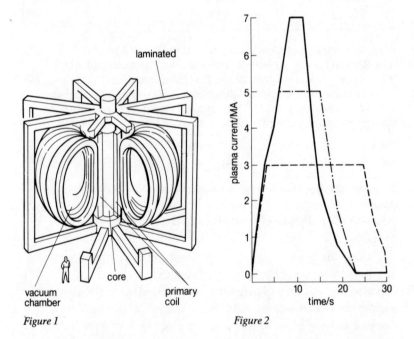

Figure 1   *Figure 2*

The large amount of electrical energy needed to produce the plasma current cannot be taken directly from the National Grid, even over the short time needed, as the power required is in excess of 700 MW. One method of storing the energy would be to use a large bank of capacitors, which could be charged up individually, then connected in parallel, and all discharged through the primary coil at the same time.

The method which is actually used in the JET programme, however, is to have two flywheel generators. Each one has a 9.0 m diameter rotor with a mass of 780 tonnes. The speed of the rotor is gradually built up to 230 rpm using an 8.8 MW motor. When a pulse of current is needed, the generator coils are connected, and each rotor slows down to half speed in a short time. If we assume that the flywheels are simple discs, the amounts of energy involved can be calculated; the rotational kinetic energy (in J) of a disc is given by $Mr^2\omega^2/4$, where M is the mass (in kg), r is the radius (in m) and ω is the angular speed (in radians/s).

(a) Explain the principle of the transformer action of the Tokamac; how can a large current be induced in the plasma by passing a much smaller current through the primary coil? (4)

(b) Most commercial transformers have two branches for the magnetic circuit of the iron. Why does the Tokamac have several? (2)

(c) Estimate the total charge that passes through the plasma as a result of the 7.0 MA current, and explain how you made your estimate. (3)

(d) If capacitors were used to provide this charge directly, and each one had a safe working voltage of 100 V, calculate the total capacitance needed and the energy stored. (4)

(e) The capacitance of a parallel plate capacitor is given by

$$C = \frac{\varepsilon_0 \varepsilon_r A}{d}$$

If ε_o is $8.9 \times 10^{-12}\,\mathrm{Fm}^{-1}$, ε_r is 3.0, and d is 0.10 mm, calculate the area A of the plates needed, and estimate the volume of capacitors needed. Why do you think the flywheel generator option was chosen? (5)

(f) Estimate the time for which the maximum current of 7.0 MA passes through the plasma, and use this with the peak power stated in the passage to calculate the energy supplied. Is the energy you calculated in question (d) of the right order of magnitude? (4)

(g) Calculate the rotational kinetic energy of one flywheel generator when spinning at its full speed, and when slowed down to half speed (1 revolution is 2π radians). Hence calculate the energy available from both generators to produce the pulse of current. (5)

(h) How long will the two 8.8 MW motors take, in theory, to bring the flywheels back to their maximum speed? Why will the actual time be longer than this? (3)

Total 30 marks

43   X-rays in dentistry

Dentistry is becoming increasingly concerned with prevention of and
early detection of decay, rather than just its treatment. One of the tools
used for this is the X-ray machine, which shows up very small areas of
decay *inside* the teeth. The X-rays are produced by bombarding a metal
target in a vacuum with high energy electrons. As the electrons are
stopped, most of their energy is transferred to the internal energy of the
target, but a small percentage is transferred to electromagnetic radiation
in the X-ray part of the spectrum. The X-ray tube is surrounded by lead
screening with just a small hole for the X-ray beam to emerge. This
point source beam is directed through the teeth onto a piece of
photographic film in a sealed plastic holder. After an exposure this film
is developed and shows the shadow of the teeth in enough detail to show
up any decay. Since X-rays are potentially harmful, the equipment and
operating procedures are regularly checked.

(a) How are free electrons produced in most electron tubes
     including X-ray tubes?   (2)
(b) Calculate the kinetic energy of an electron, charge
     1.6×10^{-19} C, after it has been accelerated by a potential
     difference of 90 kV.   (2)
(c) The tube current is 5 mA. How many electrons travel across the
     tube each second?   (2)
(d) Calculate the power of the X-ray tube.   (2)
(e) How does the target show the increase in its internal energy? (1)
(e) The most energetic X-rays are produced if an electron transfers
     all its energy in producing a single photon of radiation. If the
     energy of a photon is given by hf, calculate the frequency and
     the wavelength of the radiation. h is the Planck constant,
     6.6×10^{-34} Js, f is frequency and the speed of electromagnetic
     radiation is 3×10^8 ms^{-1}.   (4)
(f) Why must the X-ray tube behave like a point source to produce
     sharp pictures? (Hint: look at the shadows produced by a
     fluorescent tube and a single bulb light fitting.)   (3)
(g) The patient is in the full strength of the beam, but the operator
     works from more than 2 m away. Explain how this difference
     ensures that they both receive only a safe dose of radiation over
     the course of several years.   (4)

Total 20 marks

44   Gamma rays in medicine

A well known example of radioactive tracer technique in medicine is using iodine to monitor the activity of the thyroid gland. A patient is given a dose of sodium iodide, in which the iodine is the radioactive isotope, iodine–131. The body collects this iodine in the thyroid gland, and its presence is detected by the gamma radiation it gives out. An over-active thyroid would show a much larger concentration of iodine than normal, and if the dose were increased sufficiently the intensity of radiation could kill some of the thyroid gland cells, so reducing the activity to normal.

A slightly different tracer technique is used to monitor heart function. A small amount of radioactive material which does *not* interact with the body is injected into the patient's blood stream, and is carried round with the blood through the heart. Its presence is detected as before by the gamma radiation given out to the outside of the body. The detector is a 'camera' which records the position of the radioactivity nearly 60 times each second, and so a computer can reconstruct a moving picture of the blood flow and the heart action. Recently an isotope of gold, ^{195}Au*, has been produced for this use. It has a half-life of only 30 s and so the total radiation dose to the patient is very low, and if necessary the procedure can be repeated at short intervals.

(a) The iodine is given to the patient in chemical combination with sodium. Explain why this does not affect the radioactivity of the iodine in any way. *(2)*

(b) Iodine–131 emits beta and gamma radiation. Explain why only the gamma radiation is detected outside the body. *(5)*

(c) If a large enough dose is given to kill some cells, explain why the beta radiation will now play a significant part. *(2)*

(d) Iodine is element number 53. Write an equation which shows the decay of a nucleus of iodine–131. (Sb is element 51, Te is 52, Xe is 54 and Ce is 55.) *(4)*

(e) The asterisk (*) with the gold symbol denotes an excited nucleus. It is element number 79. Write an equation for its gamma decay. *(2)*

(f) Sketch the decay curve for the activity of the gold isotope over one minute, with an initial activity of 100 counts per second. Use the sketch to estimate the total number of counts in the 1 minute period. *(5)*

Total 20 marks

Radioactive nuclides such as plutonium 238 get hot as they undergo radioactive decay, since some or all of the radiation released transfers its energy to its surroundings as it is absorbed. The energy can then be transferred to electrical energy by a thermoelectric device. This effect is used in 'radioisotope thermoelectric generators', or RTG's, which have been used on spacecraft since 1961. In October 1989 the Galileo mission to Jupiter was launched. It carried two RTG's, each containing 11 kg of plutonium dioxide, (PuO_2), transferring thermal energy at a rate of 4.2 kW, and from that electrical energy at a rate of 280 W. Increasing concern about the environment made the launch newsworthy: there were fears about the consequences of an accident spreading the radioactive plutonium through the atmosphere, and many organisations campaigned for the cancellation of the launch. In the event, it went off without incident.

The basic construction of an RTG is shown below. The 'thermopile' consists of many junctions of different types of semiconductor; a potential difference is produced between the hot junctions near the plutonium and the cooler junctions away from it. (This is the same effect that occurs in the different metal junctions in a thermocouple.) Using semi-conductors means there is a significant electrical resistance for each pair of junctions, and so many of them are connected in parallel.

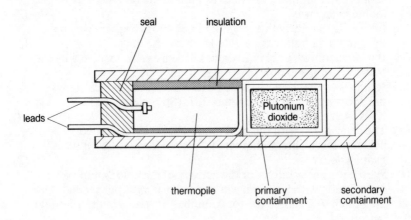

Data: Half-life of Pu–238 = 86 years
energy of alpha particle emitted = 5.5 MeV
charge on electron = 1.6×10^{-19} C
relative atomic mass Pu = 238; relative atomic mass O = 16
Avogadro's constant = 6×10^{23} mol^{-1}

(a) The plutonium is in the form of its dioxide. Explain why this
makes no difference to the radioactivity of the plutonium. *(2)*

(b) Calculate how many emissions per second are necessary to
produce the heating given in the passage. Assume that all the
radiation is absorbed in the plutonium dioxide and its primary
containment, and explain whether this is a reasonable
assumption or not. *(4)*

(c) Calculate the number of atoms of plutonium in 11 kg of
plutonium dioxide (PuO$_2$). *(2)*

(d) What proportion of the plutonium atoms is decaying to start
with, and why must the number of atoms decaying, and the
power produced, decrease? *(4)*

(e) Calculate the efficiency of the thermopile in transferring the
thermal energy to electrical energy. *(2)*

(f) The purpose of the secondary containment is not to absorb the
radiation. What *is* its purpose? *(2)*

(g) Give your own reasons why you think RTGs should, or should
not, be used for spacecraft. *(3)*

If the pairs of thermocouple junctions are connected in series, a bigger
voltage is produced, whereas if they are connected in parallel the
voltage is lower, but more current can be produced. In general the
greatest amount of energy is obtained from an electrical power supply if
it is connected to a load with the same resistance as the supply.

(h) For 10 pairs of junctions, each producing an emf of E, and each
with a resistance r, calculate for a series and for a parallel
connection
   (i) the emf
   (ii) the resistance.
Also show that the same power can be obtained from the series
and the parallel arrangement, if each arrangement is connected
to a load of the same resistance as the supply. *(8)*

(i) Suggest another application for RTGs. Explain your choice,
bearing in mind their high cost compared with more
conventional power supplies such as batteries. *(3)*

Total 30 marks

The space probe Voyager 2 flew through the Neptunian system on 24 August 1989. It had been travelling for 12 years, covered more than 7 billion kilometres and passed Jupiter, Saturn and Uranus. Most of the energy needed was given to the space probe at its launch, to get it away from the Earth. It then used the gravitational pulls of each planet in turn to help it get further and further away from the sun.

It was already known that Neptune had two moons, Triton and Nereid, but Voyager 2 discovered six more. Details of them are given in the table. Note that 1989N1 is *larger* than Nereid.

moon	diameter/km	period/hr	orbital radius/10^3 km
new:			
1989N1	420	26.9	117.6
1989N2	200	13.3	73.6
1989N3	140	8.0	52.5
1989N4	160	9.5	60.0
1989N5	90	7.5	50.0
1989N6	50	7.1	48.2
previously known:			
Triton	2720	140.9	354.3
Nereid	340	8640	5500

All the newly discovered moons are very cratered and irregular in outline. Only the largest one, 1989N1, is close to the size above which its outline would be rounded off by its own gravity.

In the following questions you may need to know that the Universal Gravitational Constant, $G = 6.67 \times 10^{-11}$ Nm^{2}kg^{-2}, and that the force F between two masses m_1 and m_2, distance r apart is given by $F = Gm_1m_2/r^2$.

(a) List the changes in potential and kinetic energy that a space probe goes through from launch to 'parking orbit', then as it moves away from Earth, and finally as it flies past a planet. *(4)*

(b) Sketch the path taken by a space probe as it flies past a planet, and indicate on it where the kinetic energy is greatest. If no fuel is used where does this energy come from? *(4)*

(c) Express the Earth's gravitational field strength g in terms of G, the mass of the Earth M and the distance from the centre of the Earth r. *(2)*

(d) Given that $g = 9.81$ Nkg^{-1} at the surface of the Earth, whose radius is 6370 km, calculate the mass of the Earth. *(2)*

(e) Calculate the energy which must be supplied to each kilogram of a space probe to enable it to escape totally from the Earth's pull. *(3)*

(f) By using the other information in the table, give a reason why 1989N1 was not discovered from Earth, even though it is bigger than Nereid. *(2)*

(g) By considering the gravitational forces on projections on an irregular but very large moon, suggest why such a moon would be 'rounded off'. *(3)*

(h) Assume that the orbits of Neptune's moons are circular. By equating the expression for the centripetal force on a moon with the gravitational attraction towards Neptune, show that the radius *r* and the period *T* of the orbit are related by

$$\frac{r^3}{T^2} = \frac{GM_N}{4\pi^2}$$

where M_N is the mass of Neptune. *(4)*

(i) Use the data in the table for 1989N1 and for Nereid with the expression in (h) to calculate the mass of Neptune. Suggest why the answers you get are not exactly the same, though the expression in (h) implies that they are. *(6)*

Total 30 marks

47   Gravity waves

The various particles of matter which make up the universe act on each other in various ways. If they are charged, for instance, they might attract or repel each other with a force known as the electromagnetic force. If they have mass, they attract each other by means of the gravitational force (there does not seem to be a repulsive version). The particles in an atomic nucleus are affected by two types of force, descriptively called the strong nuclear force and the weak nuclear force! These four forces can act over a distance (though the two nuclear ones are *very* short range). The electromagnetic force has a particle associated with it, called a photon, and the repulsion of two electrons can be reinterpreted as the exchange of this particle between them, as shown in figures 1a and 1b. In their attempts to find a unified field theory which links the four forces in a single structure, physicists have suggested, with some success, that there should be a particle associated with each force; for the strong force it is a 'gluon', for the weak force a 'W boson' (there is also a Z boson) and for the gravitational force a 'graviton'. To call photons, and the rest, particles is simplistic – they also show wave properties. The search for gluons and bosons has been carried out using particle accelerators at very high energies, but the search for gravitons from distant astronomical events such as supernovae or colliding neutron stars is being pursued in a very different way. Figure 2 shows the idea of a proposed graviton detector.

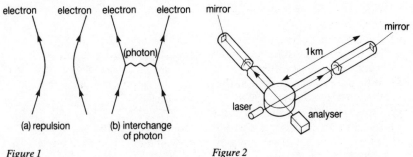

| electron   electron   electron   electron | mirror |

(photon)

(a) repulsion   (b) interchange of photon

laser   analyser   1km   mirror

Figure 1   *Figure 2*

The two arms are evacuated metal cylinders 1 km long, with a laser beam travelling along each one and back from a mirror at the far end. The laser beams are then combined with some of the original laser light to produce interference patterns. A graviton should cause a tiny change in length of either arm, of only a fraction of the wavelength of light, and this will produce a significant change in the interference pattern. The movements expected are so small that traffic vibration, seismic disturbances, and even the thermal vibration of the atoms of the tubes have to be minimised so that they do not mask the effect. The lasers proposed must also have a constant frequency, with a variation of only 1 mHz in 5×10^{14} Hz. *Two* arms at right angles mean that any time difference between changes in the interference patterns enables the direction of the gravitons to be worked out.

Data: $\dfrac{1}{4\pi\varepsilon_o} = 9 \times 10^9 \, \text{Nm}^2\text{C}^{-2}$

$G = 6.7 \times 10^{-11} \, \text{Nm}^2\text{kg}^{-2}$
mass of electron $= 9.1 \times 10^{-31}$ kg
mass of proton $= 1.7 \times 10^{-27}$ kg
charge on electron $= 1.6 \times 10^{-19}$ C
charge on a proton $= +1.6 \times 10^{-19}$ C
speed of light $= 3 \times 10^8 \, \text{ms}^{-1}$

Relationship:
force between charges q_1 and q_2 distance r apart $= \dfrac{1}{4\pi\varepsilon_o} \dfrac{q_1 q_2}{r^2}$

force between masses m_1 and m_2 distance r apart $= \dfrac{Gm_1 m_2}{r^2}$

(a) Calculate the electrical force between an electron and a proton if they are 10^{-10} m apart. *(3)*

(b) Calculate the gravitational force between the electron and proton in part (a). *(3)*

(c) What is the ratio between the electrical and the gravitational forces in (a) and (b)? *(2)*

(d) The nucleus of a gold atom is made up of 79 protons and 118 neutrons, and alpha particles fired at a gold leaf can be strongly repelled from a nucleus (as in Geiger and Marsden's famous experiment). How do these facts tell you that the strong nuclear force is stronger than the electromagnetic force and that it is short range? *(6)*

(e) Give reasons why a remote part of Scotland has been suggested for the graviton detector, and why the arms should be cooled to a very low temperature. *(6)*

(f) Why does the frequency of the laser light proposed to measure the length of the arms have to be so stable? *(2)*

(g) Calculate the wavelength of the light. *(2)*

(h) If a shift of $\frac{1}{20}$ of a wavelength can be detected in the interference pattern, what percentage change in length of an arm can be measured? *(3)*

(i) From which directions could gravitons be arriving if the changes were detected simultaneously? *(3)*

Total 30 marks

Answers to numerical questions

1   (c) 80 Nm   (e) 2.5 m, 500 J   (f) 10^5N

2   (b) 2.2 ms^{-1}, 440 ms^{-1} (f) 8.2 cm, 2.4 cm

3   (b) 8000 N

4   (g) 45 N

8   (e) steel 4.8×10^{-3}%, rubber 20%

9   (d) 0.4 mm

10   (d) 5×10^6 Pa

11   (a) 10 J   (b) 4.35×10^{-5}, 4.31×10^{-7} (c) 1.01×10^7 Pa
(e) 216 J   (f) 4.6%

12   (a) 26 000 L (26 m^3)   (b) 0.19 m^3 (c) 140 atmospheres

13   (f) Energy stored in rubber approx. 6× that in skin.

15   (d)(i) 10^{-3} (ii) 2×10^8 Nm^{-2} (iii) 25 N (iv) 10^{-3} kgm^{-1} (v)
1600 Hz   (e) 12.5 N   (f) 1100 Hz

16   (a) 9.1×10^{13} Hz   (c) 560 Nm^{-1} (d) 2.3×10^{-6} m

17   (f) 10^{10} Hz   (g) 600 Hz   (h) 10 mph

18   (a) 24 h   (d) 81°   (g) 5.7°

19   (a) 35 μs, 64 μs, 86 μs, each ±1 μs   (b) 7 km, 12.8 km, 17.2 km,
each ±200 m

20   (d)(i) ±10° (ii) ±20° (iii) ±6°

21   (g)(i) 2000 (ii) 2000.5 (iii) 1.9995×10^8 ms^{-1}

22   (b) 2.45×10^{-19} J   (c) 2.27×10^{14} Hz, 2.82×10^{14} Hz,
3.17×10^{14} Hz   (e) 1.50×10^{-19} J, 1.86×10^{-19} J,
2.09×10^{-19} J   (g) 16.5°

23   (c) 2 mm   (d) 10 ms^{-1} (g) 5×10^{14} Hz   (h) 1.0 ms^{-1}

24   (e) 0.13°

28   (b) 2.5 μH

29   (a) 4.2×10^{-5} Ω, 2.3 kg   (b) 2.3 cm, 3.6 kg   (h) 23 kN   (j) 17 kN

30   (f) 3.2 Hz

31   (a) 18 : 1, 330 times   (e) 6000 km, 1500 km